The Design of Fire Detection Installations for Dwellings

A guide to BS 5839-6: 2004

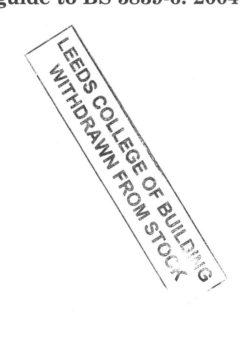

The Design of Fire Detection Installations for Dwellings

A Guide to BS 5839-6: 2004

Colin S. Todd

Business
Information

The Design of Fire Detection Installations for Dwellings
A Guide to BS 5839-6: 2004

First published by Paramount Publishing Ltd. 1996
This edition published by BSi 2004

© British Standards Institution 2004

ISBN 0 580 44016 8

BSI reference: BIP 2044

The right of Colin S. Todd to be identified as the author of this work
has been asserted in accordance with the Copyright, Designs and
Patents Act 1988.

A catalogue record for this book is available from the British Library.

Typeset by Monolith – www.monolith.uk.com
Printed by PIMS Digital

Dedicated to my three children,
Keith, Jayne and Fiona.

Contents

About the author

Colin Todd MSc, FIFireE, FBEng, MIRM, MSFPE, C.Phys, MInstP, C.Eng, FIEE, graduated from Edinburgh University with an honours degree in Physics. He then undertook a one-year Masters degree in Fire Safety Engineering, developing a specific interest in the quantitative assessment of risk, mathematical modelling and systems engineering.

In 1975, he joined the captive insurance company of Unilever Ltd. As a member of the risk management section, he carried out regular fire surveys of Unilever premises and was responsible for providing in-house advice on loss prevention matters. He later joined the technical department of the Fire Offices' Committee (FOC), which dealt with the preparation of codes and standards on fire protection and approvals of fire protection equipment. With the FOC he specialised in electrical matters, and was responsible for assessing the suitability of fire alarm equipment for FOC approval. During this time he represented the FOC on national committees including those of the BSI. (The FOC was later incorporated into the Loss Prevention Council.)

Colin Todd is a chartered engineer and a Fellow of the Institution of Electrical Engineers, the Association of Building Engineers and the Institution of Fire Engineers. He is a corporate member of the Institute of Physics and the Society of Fire Protection Engineers. He is also a standards associate of the British Standards Society.

As the final President of the UK Chapter of the Society of Fire Protection Engineers, he was instrumental in the merger between that organization and the Society of Fire Safety Engineers to form the Institute of Fire Safety, on the council of which he then served. Subsequently, the Institute of Fire Safety was absorbed into the Institution of Fire Engineers (IFE) to form the basis of the Engineering Council Division (ECD) of the IFE. Currently, Colin is Chairman of the Membership Committee of the Engineering Council Division of the IFE, which awards the qualification of Chartered Engineer, Incorporated Engineer and Engineering Technician to suitably qualified and experienced fire engineers. Colin also serves on a number of British Standards Committees, including those concerned with fire detection and alarm systems. He also represents the Confederation of British Industry on Expert Group A of the Loss Prevention Certification Board (part of BRE Certification), which is responsible for the development of approval schemes for all aspects of automatic fire alarm equipment.

Preface

This book gives an insight into the thinking behind the BS code of practice for the design, installation and maintenance of fire detection and alarm systems in dwellings (BS 5839-6). The need for the book does not arise from any deficiencies in the Code; it arises from the fact that users of the Code often wish to know why particular clauses have been put into the Code.

Achieving a suitable design for occupancies such as houses in multiple occupation and sheltered housing requires a detailed understanding of fire protection principles. Even in relatively small dwellings a number of engineering judgements have to be made. This book aids specifiers, designers and installers in making those judgements.

In 1994, the author of the book, Colin Todd, was contracted by the British Standards Institution to write the first draft of BS 5839-6. Subsequently, in 2003, he was contracted to draft the first major revision of the Code, which is the subject of this book. He is a member of the BSI technical committee responsible for the Code, being the Institution of Fire Engineers' representative on the committee. Because of this, he was party to all the discussions concerning the Code's development and is thus ably qualified to expand on and explain the content of the Code. The interpretations given in this guide are, of course, Colin Todd's but, naturally, they benefit from Colin's close involvement in the development of the Code.

J W Northey
Chairman, BSI Technical Committee FSH/12,
Fire Detection and Alarm Systems

1. Introduction

The aim of this book is to provide guidance on what, at the time of writing, is a newly revised version of BS 5839-6. The new (2004) version supersedes the earlier (1995) version, and incorporates major changes, not just in detail, but also in philosophy.

The Code, which, as one part of the BS 5839 suite of codes and standards, bears the generic heading 'Fire detection and fire alarm systems for buildings', is entitled 'Code of practice for the design, installation and maintenance of fire detection and fire alarm systems in dwellings'. As such, it is to this Code that designers, suppliers, installers, regulatory authorities and consultants will turn in order to obtain guidance on good practice in respect of the provision of automatic fire detection in any type of dwelling, from a small flat to a stately home.

To many of us in the fire engineering profession, the design of fire precautions in most dwellings may lack the engineering challenge of the design of fire safety in more complex occupancies. However, it is easy to forget that the vast majority of fire deaths in the United Kingdom still occur in dwellings. Whether this is because of the attention to fire precautions that goes into the design of non-domestic buildings, leaving dwellings as something of a forgotten and final frontier for fire engineering, or whether it is simply the greater inherent risk associated with dwellings and their occupants, is a moot point; I suspect a bit of both.

However, there is no uncertainty in the benefit of domestic fire detection to the safety of life from fire. Indeed, I believe it would be no exaggeration to say that the domestic smoke detector is one of the greatest success stories in the last half century of fire protection, such has been the impact on loss of life. It is unfortunate that the media have never seemed to consider this success to be of major interest to the general public; perhaps success is less newsworthy than gloom and doom! Even in these days when every item of expenditure seems to come under the most stringent scrutiny, I believe that expenditure to date on domestic smoke detection can be shown to be cost effective in terms of lives saved, given typical figures quoted for the value of a human life.

So domestic fire detection is successful and here to stay, but does it really warrant a comprehensive engineering code of practice, particularly as many 'systems' in dwellings still comprise nothing more than battery-operated smoke alarms installed by the occupier. The background to the production of BS 5839-6 will be examined more closely in the next chapter. Suffice to say at this stage that not only is the Code warranted, but that support for legislation, particularly building regulations, with a detailed and definitive code of practice is actually essential. Moreover, although we tend to think of a house (or dwelling) as a simple three- or four-bedroom house at most, I would suggest that Windsor Castle and Buckingham Palace are houses (possibly in multiple occupation)! Indeed, case law abounds as to what, in law, actually constitutes a house and a house in multiple occupation (HMO). Happily, in using the code of practice, it will rarely, if ever, be necessary to engage in such pedantry, albeit that it can be a source of substantial income for the legal profession.

Particular occupancies, such as sheltered housing, HMOs and large mansions all require a relatively detailed understanding of fire protection principles if the fire detection systems installed in them are to be suitably designed. However, even in relatively small dwellings, there are a number of engineering judgements to be made in respect of the form of protection that is to be provided. For example, will battery-operated smoke alarms be sufficiently reliable? Unfortunately, it is now the case that deaths are occurring in dwellings protected by such devices, from which batteries have been removed because of an inability to pay for replacements, frequent false alarms and 'borrowing' the batteries for use in other household appliances or toys. If we use mains-operated smoke alarms, should we connect them on their own circuit or is it acceptable to connect them on, say, an existing lighting circuit? How many smoke alarms or smoke detectors do we actually need in any case? Is it sufficient to install them just in the hallways and landings or might we need them in some rooms as well? There is a need to address such questions in some detail as domestic fire detection more and more becomes the norm rather than an unusual accessory, and these matters are fully considered in the Code.

As the author of both the first draft of BS 5839-6, and the draft of the latest version, it might be argued that I failed to draft a sufficiently simple code of practice if a guide, such as this, to the Code is warranted! In fact, I believe that the Code should, for most circumstances, prove simple and straightforward to use. Some may argue that the Code, at first reading, seems rather complicated for something as simple as dwellings. However, this is a result of the very comprehensive nature of the Code and the consequent need to provide guidance on both life safety and property protection in the very wide range of buildings that may constitute dwellings of one kind or another. It is also necessary for the Code to acknowledge the numerous different forms of fire detection 'system' that are currently available, ranging from one or more battery-operated smoke alarms to comprehensive new technology systems of the type described in BS 5839-1[1]. As in the case of any British Standard, the Code does not hypothesise on what might become available, but merely reflects on what is offered on the marketplace today and the recognized good practices that are associated with the different types of equipment.

Given that it is then necessary to 'match' system type to application – for example limiting the use of the simpler systems to smaller and lower risk properties – the Code at first sight may seem something of a cultural shock, bearing in mind that other available guidance is restricted to a few basic design requirements in the guidance that supports building regulations and a guide to householders produced by the Office of the Deputy Prime Minister. However, I hope that when it comes to applying the Code to any particular dwelling, using any particular type of fire detection installation, the Code should provide simple and definitive advice.

Even so, since the new version of the Code effectively takes domestic fire detection a step forward and introduces new standards for the protection of dwellings by automatic fire detection, I hope that this guide will provide some insight into its recommendations and help to ensure that the philosophy behind the recommendations is accurately implemented in future installations. Since the new version of the Code is in its infancy, it will, no doubt, suffer from some teething problems. Unforeseen circumstances will inevitably arise when its recommendations are not entirely appropriate, such as when types of fire detection system that do not fall neatly into one of the 'Grades' defined in the Code become available.

However, as a code of practice, it is accepted that, in some circumstances, variations from the recommendations of the Code may be appropriate; the Code itself caters for such variations. As experience in the use of the Code grows and any anomalies come to light, amendments may be necessary. If users of the Code consider that an amendment to a code or standard may be necessary, or that some clarification may be required, it is always worthwhile writing to the BSI committee responsible for its production, in this case committee FSH/12/1. My experience of BSI committees is that all such comments, whether from a major installer, a small electrical contractor, a single independent consultant or whoever, are always given

---

[1] BS 5839-1: 2002. *Fire detection and fire alarm systems for buildings – Code of practice for system design, installation, commissioning and maintenance.*

serious consideration, and it is from such comments that codes of practice sometimes develop and keep pace with custom and practice.

Obviously, this guide is not a substitute for the Code itself, but should be read in conjunction with the Code. The guide should not be regarded as offering any final authoritative interpretation on any recommendations of the Code, although I hope that the opinions expressed are an accurate reflection of the committee's intent when the Code was published. If it is essential to obtain a definitive interpretation, such as in the event of a dispute, advice may be sought from BSI, who will refer the matter to the relevant committee. Ultimately, the final arbiter in such a dispute can, however, only be the Courts. Hopefully, BS 5839-6 will prove sufficiently unambiguous that such disputes will be extremely rare.

As discussed in the next chapter, domestic fire detection has made a significant impact on fire deaths in dwellings, which account for around 80% of all fire deaths. It is relatively cheap in relation to the enhancement in life safety it can provide. It can protect those in society who are most vulnerable to fire, namely the elderly and the very young. Personally, as a parent, I have always been reluctant to permit my children to stay overnight with friends unless the house has smoke alarms, particularly if I know that members of the family are likely to smoke.

However, if the full potential of this important form of fire protection is to be realized, long-term reliability and continued use must be ensured by proper system design, appropriate installation practices and the avoidance of unnecessary false alarms. The new version of BS 5839-6 will go a long way towards achievement of this objective. As recently as ten years ago, a family saved from fire by the early warning from a smoke alarm was newsworthy. Hopefully, by the time BS 5839-6 is ready for its next revision, the death of a family due to the absence of properly designed and installed fire detection will be sufficiently unusual to be equally newsworthy.

2. Domestic fire detection – a short history

In the United Kingdom, domestic fire detection is a relatively recent innovation. However, in the USA, self-contained domestic fire detectors first became available in 1955 – nearly fifty years ago! However, these devices were heat detectors and were relatively insensitive, even compared with the heat detectors available today. They were mechanically powered and used either compressed gas or a wound spring as a source of energy to operate an audible alarm that formed an integral part of the device.

The earliest relevant standard for domestic fire detection installations was probably the American National Fire Protection Association (NFPA) standard, NFPA 74 (Household Fire Warning Equipment), which was first published in 1967. The development of this standard followed withdrawal of an earlier document (NFPA 74M), entitled Manual on Home Fire Alarm Systems, the first version of which appeared as a two-page document in 1950. Since the original publication of NFPA 74, the standard has been revised very significantly several times. In studying BS 5839-6, one can find evidence of only the most minor influence of the NFPA standard, since the British Code is based more on current custom and practice in the United Kingdom and, to some extent, the thinking embodied in BS 5839-1. However, this is not to say that the practices adopted in the UK and the USA are necessarily inconsistent.

The original NFPA standard was based on practices adopted in industrial and commercial premises, whereby there was general coverage by detectors throughout protected premises. Therefore, the standard required that there be at least one heat detector in every room and a smoke detector outside the bedrooms. These detectors were of the conventional 'system' type, necessitating the provision of control and indicating equipment, which could power and monitor the heat and smoke detectors. Because of the cost of such installations (estimated at $1,500 for a small house at then current prices), they were few in number – it has been estimated that fewer than 1% of homes in the USA were protected in this manner.

Self-contained smoke alarms as we know them today were first produced in the USA during the latter half of the 1960s. The earliest types produced were mains-powered optical detectors, but towards the end of the decade, battery-powered ionization chamber smoke detectors were produced. During the 1960s, a number of tests led to the conclusion that smoke detectors in circulation spaces could, in some fires at least, give an earlier warning than heat detectors in the room of origin, albeit that the tests tended to use open plan layouts.

In 1974, NFPA 74 accepted two important principles. Firstly, that it might not be necessary to install a detector within every room in a dwelling. Secondly, and consequent to the latter philosophy, different 'levels of protection' could be defined. While the highest level, level 1, was consistent with the earlier requirements of NFPA 74, the lowest level, level 4, required only a single smoke detector outside the bedrooms and a further smoke detector at the top of any basement staircase.

Support for the use of smoke detectors in circulation spaces comes from the conclusions of the 'Indiana Dunes' tests, which were carried out in three real houses, which were intended for demolition, during the 1970s. Following these tests, the 1978 version of NFPA 74 defined the minimum standard as smoke detection on every level of a house.

By the late 1970s, a number of states in the USA required the installation of smoke detection in new dwellings under local building codes. There are in fact many thousands of state, city or county building codes in the USA, but it is now the case that all state codes require the installation of smoke detection in dwellings (and indeed other sleeping risks). In practice, whether under a state code or other local building code, all new dwellings in the USA must be protected by smoke detection. Perhaps more interestingly, most such codes require this retrospectively in existing dwellings. However, enforcement of the retrospective requirement is very limited – there are no inspections, although occasionally a house owner is prosecuted if, for example, there is a serious fire and it is discovered that the house has no smoke detection.

In 1993, the requirements of NFPA 74 were incorporated in the new National Fire Alarm Code, NFPA 72, and it is this standard to which building codes now refer. According to a 1999 NFPA study, 95% of US housing is protected by at least one smoke alarm, although sadly it has been estimated that nearly 40% of domestic fires reported that year occurred in the remaining 5% of housing stock. Given the long experience of domestic smoke alarms in the United States, it is also interesting to consider the effect smoke alarms have had on fire deaths. According to the NFPA, from 1980, a time when smoke alarm requirements were starting to become common, fire deaths have fallen from 6,500 to 3,400 in 2002.

It has been estimated that the effect of 100% compliance with the NFPA standard throughout the USA would result in a 50% drop in fire deaths. NFPA estimates the death rate per 100 fires is generally 40% to 50% lower in homes with smoke alarms than in homes without them.

In the UK, we will note in a later chapter that the British Standard attempts to move things forward from the simple battery-operated smoke alarm to smoke alarms and smoke detection systems of higher reliability. This mirrors progress in the USA, where the NFPA standard accepts battery-powered detectors only for retrofitting in existing homes, but requires mains-powered devices for new homes. Since the 1996 edition, the NFPA 72 National Fire Alarm Code has required mains-powered smoke alarms with a standby supply for new homes.

As in the UK, there is experience in the USA that smoke alarms are not being adequately maintained. In this context, clearly battery-operated devices present the greatest potential for failure. In 1995, the Consumer Product Safety Commission in the USA released the results of their National Smoke Detection Project. It was found that, when initially tested, about one third of detectors (mains and battery-operated) did not function. When the power supplies were reconnected, approximately one half of the detectors then functioned correctly. The NFPA now estimate that households with non-working smoke alarms outnumber those with no smoke alarms. Of particular interest was the fact that most of those that initially failed to function had been intentionally disconnected due to false alarms. This study has a clear message in terms of the effect of false alarms on user attitude towards smoke alarms, and the importance, in effect, to life safety of minimizing false alarms. The approach of BS 5839-6 to this problem is discussed in a later chapter.

In the United Kingdom, smoke alarms first became available in the 1970s. The first devices were generally of the battery-operated type and were imported from the USA. The cost, which was sometimes as high as £45 per unit, was relatively expensive compared with today's prices of just a few pounds.

Initially, there was no great enthusiasm for smoke alarms, and various obstacles to their widespread usage were sometimes expressed. These included the differences in construction of American and British dwellings, a perception that nation-wide use would not be cost effective, concerns of users over false alarms and, of course, the relatively high cost to the individual householder, the highest risk category of whom would be unable to afford such a perceived non-essential.

By 1987, only 9% of all houses in England and Wales were protected by even a single smoke alarm. However, active campaigns by individual fire brigades and, more particularly, vigorous central Government funded advertising began to take effect in the latter part of the 1980s. The year 1988, in particular, was a time of enormous growth in smoke alarm sales.

In 1988, the Home Departments published guidance for householders, entitled 'Smoke Alarms in the Home'. This booklet was also reproduced as an Appendix to BS 5839-1: 1988. As demand for smoke alarms grew, the prices fell dramatically; as prices fell, more householders, convinced by fire brigade/Home Office campaigns, felt able to justify the cost, and the upward spiral of demand along with the downward spiral in cost was inexorable. Ionization chamber detectors were the cheaper, and so were in greater demand than optical detectors. The law of supply and demand caused the differential to increase to an extent that the current differential in price is around 3:1 in the case of battery-operated devices, although only about 30% in the case of mains-operated smoke alarms. As discussed in a later chapter, the guidance contained in BS 5839-6 may tend to result in increased sales of optical detectors and thus a decrease in price differential.

The first available guidance in the form of 'Smoke Alarms in the Home' implied that one smoke alarm might be sufficient in a multi-storey house, although it was made clear that two or more would offer more reliable early warning and greater time to escape; the intention was clearly to ensure that some affordable protection was provided in as many dwellings as possible. The Government were, however, still reluctant to make the installation of smoke alarms compulsory in normal, single-family dwellings.

In other, higher risk dwellings, the situation was rather different. In this connection, a particularly 'live' issue, and one that remains a current issue today, is the problem of fire safety in HMOs. In 1985, a working party established by the then Institute of Environmental Health Officers (now the Chartered Institute of Environmental Health) determined that the risk of dying in a fire for those living in HMOs was between eight and ten times the risk of dying in a single-family dwelling. However, in England and Wales, the relevant legislation, namely the Housing Act 1985, permitted local authorities to require only adequate means of escape; there were no powers to require fire detection and alarm systems (or emergency lighting, fire extinguishing appliances, etc.). The Act was, nevertheless, amended by the Local Government and Housing Act 1989 to enable the local authority to require other 'fire precautions', which is generally accepted to include automatic fire detection and alarm systems. (Unfortunately, because of a transfer of responsibility for guidance on fire precautions in HMOs from the Home Office to the Department of the Environment, it was 1992 before suitable guidance on the standards that should be required was made available in the form of Department of the Environment Circular 12/92.) Subsequent research carried out on behalf of the Government, and published in 1997, suggests that the risk of dying from fire is actually highly variable across the many very different types of properties that constitute HMOs. Some findings of this research were taken into account in the drafting of the new version of BS 5839-6.

So this special category of high risk dwellings could be required to have automatic fire detection under powers granted by legislation. In 1990, further support for the use of smoke alarms and, in the case of certain dwellings, complete fire detection systems complying with BS 5839-1, came in the form of BS 5588-1[2], which recommended that self-contained smoke alarms (requirements for the performance of which had been incorporated in BS 5446-1[3] during the same year) or a BS 5839-1 system be installed in all dwellings. In 1993, BS 5588-1 was amended to recommend that, in the case of smoke alarms, these should be mains-powered. For certain dwellings (sheltered housing, flats in a mixed user development that is protected by an automatic fire detection and alarm system and large private dwellings, such as country mansions), BS 5588-1 specifically recommends a fire detection and alarm system complying with BS 5839-1. (Unfortunately, the advice in BS 5839-6 and that in BS 5588-1, particularly in respect of sheltered housing, is not entirely consistent.)

However, undoubtedly the greatest impetus to the future use of smoke detection in dwellings came in the form of proposals that all new dwellings should be required by legislation to be protected in this manner. In 1991, the then MP for York, Mr Conal Gregory, appalled by the deaths and injuries in dwellings, introduced a Private Members Bill, the Smoke Detectors Bill, requiring smoke detection in all dwellings. This Bill received all-party support, but there was concern over any retrospective requirements that it might contain.

Ultimately, the Smoke Detectors Act 1991 received the Royal Assent in July of that year, and required that smoke detectors be installed in all new dwellings in England and Wales. However, the Act was framed in such a way that it would be brought into effect only when the Home Secretary so determined by means of an order contained in a statutory instrument. The Government took the view that the matter should be dealt with by the then Department of Environment through the Building Regulations, and therefore no such statutory instrument has ever been issued; the Smoke

---

[2] BS 5588-1: 1990. *Fire precautions in the design, construction and use of buildings – Code of practice for residential buildings.*

[3] BS 5446-1: 1990. *Components of automatic fire alarm systems for residential premises – Specification for self-contained smoke alarms and point-type smoke detectors.* (Now superseded by the 2000 version – see below.)

BS 5446-1: 2000. *Fire detection and fire alarm devices for dwellings. Specification for smoke alarms.*

Detectors Act therefore remains in limbo, and has never been brought into effect. It is likely that, in 2005, it will be repealed by the Regulatory Reform (Fire safety Order) (in draft form at the time of writing).

Instead, the then DoE addressed the matter of smoke detection in dwellings as part of their revision of the Building Regulations and the guidance that supports them. The Building Regulations 1991, which came into force in June 1992, required that all dwellings should be provided with adequate means of escape (Requirement B1 of Schedule 1 to the Regulations made this requirement in respect of all buildings to which the Regulations apply, except prisons). Approved Document B, which supports the Regulations by setting out the normal means of compliance with their requirements, then specified that dwellings should be protected by either an automatic fire detection and alarm system complying with the recommendations of BS 5839-1 for a Type L3 system or be provided with a suitable number of mains-operated smoke alarms that conform to BS 5446-1.

Technically, therefore, at that time, there was not a specific requirement within the Building Regulations (or any other legislation) in England and Wales to provide smoke detectors in all new dwellings. It was simply the case that smoke detection was generally deemed necessary to satisfy Requirement B1. The requirement for smoke detection did not, however, sit comfortably as one of the provisions for adequate means of escape. Moreover, in theory, it would have been acceptable to demonstrate that adequate means of escape was provided by some other means. This somewhat inelegant means by which smoke detection was required in new dwellings in England and Wales ceased to exist after the year 2000. In that year, amendments to the Building Regulations 1991 (which later became the Building Regulations 2000) incorporated a new Regulation B1, which required that, in all premises within the scope of the Regulations (including dwellings), there must be not only adequate means of escape in case of fire, but also appropriate provisions for the early warning of fire. The requirement for fire detection systems in dwellings (and some form of giving fire warning in all premises) thus became much more explicit.

An amended Approved Document B (2000 version) continued to provide the supporting guidance on the means of compliance with Regulation B1. The guidance does, however, somewhat undermine BS 5839-6; even though the guidance refers to BS 5839-6, as an alternative to compliance with the Code Approved Document B accepts compliance with 19 specific paragraphs in the Approved Document (other than in the case of large dwellings, for which a system complying with BS 5839-1 is advocated). Of course, these paragraphs cannot possibly reflect all the technical recommendations of BS 5839-6, which had been developed primarily to support the Building Regulations.

Now a new BS 5839-6 has been published, and has the support of the Government Department responsible for the Building Regulations, namely the Office of the Deputy Prime Minister (ODPM), who are represented on the BSI technical committee responsible for BS 5839-6. It is, therefore, to be hoped that, when Approved Document B is next revised, it will simply refer to compliance with BS 5839-6, rather than offering the option of a 'short-cut' to compliance with Regulation B1.

In Scotland, the situation has always been much simpler. Smoke detection in new dwellings was first required when the Building Standards (Scotland) Regulations 1990 were amended by the Building Standards (Scotland) Amendment Regulations 1993 to include a specific requirement that every dwelling be provided with adequate means of warning the occupants in the event of fire. (Subsequent amendments extended this to all residential accommodation and enclosed shopping centres.) The Technical Standards that support the Regulations set out 'deemed to satisfy' standards for the necessary fire detection. These requirements are broadly in line with the recommendations of BS 5839-6 for a Grade D Category LD3 system (other than in the case of large dwellings, for which a BS 5839-1 system is required), but all the recommendations of BS 5839-6 need not be satisfied. Instead, the Technical Standards simply set out about half an A4 page of technical requirements drawn from BS 5839-6.

In Northern Ireland, the situation began as something between that in England and Wales and that in Scotland. In 1993, the Building (Amendment) Regulations (Northern Ireland) 1993 amended the Building Regulations (Northern Ireland) 1990 to make specific and detailed requirements in respect of smoke detection in dwellings. These requirements were, again, similar to the advice contained in Approved Document B. Subsequently, in the Building Regulations (Northern Ireland) 1994 (now the Building Regulations (Northern Ireland) 2000), the requirement was cast in a more functional form, but was still more specific in relation to fire detection and alarm than the Regulations in England and Wales. The current requirement under the Regulations in Northern Ireland is that, for all buildings, in the event of fire, there must be adequate means of giving warning and, where appropriate, adequate means of automatic detection. The supporting guidance is set out in Technical Booklet E 1994 (as amended in 2000), published by the Department of the Environment (Northern Ireland). The approach is very similar to Approved Document B, in that, (other than in large dwellings), it is possible to follow just six paragraphs in the Technical Booklet, rather than adopting BS 5839-6 in its entirety. However, as in Scotland, mains-operated smoke alarms in new dwellings in Northern Ireland must have a standby supply; this is not the case in England and Wales.

The three sets of building regulations have given rise to certain difficulties. For example, the reference to a Type L3 system in accordance with BS 5839-1, which occurs in all three supporting documents, implies that if, instead of smoke alarms, a BS 5839-1 system is installed, detectors should be installed in all rooms opening onto the circulation areas, which could mean virtually all rooms in the house. Clearly, this is not what was intended, since, in the case of smoke alarms, only the circulation areas need to be protected to satisfy the requirements. The problem arose because L3 was the lowest life safety designation recognized in BS 5839-1: 1988, but, in order to protect escape routes, that code advised that detectors should be installed in all rooms adjoining the escape routes; this standard of protection was intended for situations such as hotel corridors, rather than domestic buildings. It might now be more appropriate, in the case of normal-sized dwellings, for which, in excess of the minimum requirements, a BS 5839-1: 2002 system is proposed, for the guidance that supports building regulations to refer to the new Category L5 system defined in the 2002 version of BS 5839-1, with specific additional guidance on the areas in which detectors are to be installed.

A more specific inconsistent detail in these sets of Regulations is the form of electrical supply to smoke alarms. All require mains-powered devices but, whereas, as noted above, in Scotland and Northern Ireland a standby supply (battery or capacitor) is required, in England and Wales 'mains only' smoke alarms without any standby supply are acceptable. Since BS 5839-6 recommends the provision of a standby supply for smoke alarms in all new dwellings, it is likely that this will also be specified in the next revision of Approved Document B.

However, regardless of the finer detail of the requirements and their status, the recognition of the need for smoke detection in dwellings has enhanced the status of domestic smoke detection as an essential life safety measure. In the short period between 1987 and 2003, the percentage of homes in England and Wales protected by smoke alarms rose from 9% to 81%, although this is obviously more the result of public education and awareness than new house building *per se*.

The mains-operated smoke alarms specified in the Regulations became readily available in the latter half of the 1980s, and have clearly made an important contribution to detector reliability. A Home Office study of battery-operated smoke alarms in 10,000 houses in the Tameside Region of Greater Manchester showed that, three years after installation, 11% of smoke alarms were ineffective. In 30% of these cases, batteries were either missing or flat. It is now generally accepted that mains-operated devices with a standby supply dominate sales, particularly amongst local authorities, for whose housing stock BS 5839-6 recommends against battery-operated smoke alarms, even for retrofitting, except in the case of single-storey dwellings, such as flats and bungalows, for which smoke alarms powered by 'long life' batteries are considered acceptable.

As a code of practice, BS 5839-6 in general simply reflects good standards of custom and practice in the marketplace today. However, in a number of respects it also 'pushes out the boat' in terms of a number of aspects of design, with the intent of moving domestic fire detection forward. For example, concepts first introduced in the 1995 version of the Code include the use of mini-systems (as opposed purely to self-contained smoke alarms), integrated fire and intruder alarm systems, wireless (radio-based) systems and, in terms of system performance, better designed installations that will be less susceptible to false alarms. There is now much greater emphasis on avoidance of false alarms in the 2004 version of the Code.

In the 2004 version of BS 5839-6, the much greater specification of standby power supplies for mains-operated smoke alarms is one example of the manner in which domestic fire detection will move further forward as a result of the revision of BS 5839-6. Perhaps more importantly, the 2004 version of the Code recommends that, for all new dwellings, detectors should be installed not just in the circulation areas, but in the kitchen and the 'principal habitable room' (i.e. normal living room). This will further improve the standard of fire protection in new dwellings at almost negligible cost.

In the UK, the pace of development in the use of domestic smoke detection has been rapid, with battery-operated smoke alarms, which were quite 'new fangled gadgets' to most people only a decade ago, now beginning to look almost old fashioned. There is no doubt that the next decade will see further significant developments in the technology and practices associated with domestic fire detection.

The author is grateful to the following people for information on the history of domestic fire detection standards in the USA:

Mr. R. W. Bukowski, Senior Research Engineer at the National Institute of Standards and Technology's Building and Fire Research Laboratory in Gaithersburg, MD, USA.
Mr L. Richardson, Senior Electrical Engineer, National Fire Protection Association.
Ms M. Ahrens, Fire Analysis Specialist, National Fire Protection Association.

3. Scope of BS 5839-6

The recommendations of BS 5839-6 basically apply to any form of fire detection installed in any premises that would, in common parlance (as opposed to a strict legal context), be described as a house or dwelling, with the possible exception of some houses that are converted into hostel-type accommodation. There will certainly be very few, if any, forms of conventional single-family (or 'single-household') accommodation that do not come within the scope of the Code, whether or not such units are independent, or part of larger premises. Moreover, unlike many British Standards, which are clearly not intended to be retrospective, this Code gives guidance on the protection of existing, as well as new, dwellings. However, nowhere does the Code suggest that existing fire detection and alarm systems in dwellings should be upgraded. It is more the case, therefore, that the retrospective nature of the Code relates to new fire detection systems for existing dwellings.

The 'systems' covered by the Code

Let us consider first though the forms of fire detection to which the Code applies. Before we actually open the Code to read it, the use of the term 'fire detection and fire alarm systems' in the title might, at first, mislead us; we might think that the Code applies only to 'systems' in the sense that the term is used in BS 5839-1, i.e. systems comprising control and indicating equipment, fire detectors and independent alarm sounders. In fact, nothing could be further from the truth, as is implied, if not expressly stated, in the Foreword to the Code, which explains that BS 5839-1 does not provide recommendations for fire detection and fire alarm systems in dwellings.

However, the very first clause of BS 5839-6 removes any ambiguity. Clause 1 (Scope) advises that the 'systems' covered by the Code range from a single self-contained smoke alarm (which could be battery-operated) to complete systems of the type to which BS 5839-1 applies. Moreover, lest it be thought that the application of the word 'system' to a single battery-operated smoke alarm is something of a contradiction, it should be pointed out that the term 'fire detection and fire alarm system' is defined in clause 3 (Definitions). The definition for the purpose of BS 5839-6 is a:

> 'system that comprises a means for automatically detecting one of the characteristic phenomena of fire and a means for providing a warning to occupants.'

A note to the definition makes it clear that this definition is intended to include 'systems' that comprise one or more smoke alarms as well as, of course, the 'systems' to which the term is more commonly applied.

An important point to note from clause 1 is that the recommendations of the Code may be applied to the fire detection part of a combined fire/intruder alarm system or a fire/social alarm system. (Social alarm systems are alarm systems installed in the homes of elderly and disabled people to enable them to summon help in an emergency.) This is important to note because we may well see much greater use of such integrated systems, particularly those integrating fire and intruder detection, in the future.

This will, arguably, be a very good thing because it could potentially enable us to have slightly more sophisticated domestic fire detection systems, with a higher degree of monitoring and control, on the back of the intruder alarm system that occupiers will much more readily install. After all, the public perceive burglary as a much greater risk than fire and, in the sense of the greater chance of occurrence, they are probably correct in this perception. Intruder alarm systems are no longer an accessory of the large houses of the rich – just count the bell boxes in any typical row of back to backs in any large town. Because of the mass market, the cost of control panels has dropped considerably.

Unfortunately, the public perception of fire risk is unlikely to create a mass market for domestic fire alarm control panels (although such a panel is described in an Annex to BS 5839-6). However, fire detection as a value added facility in an intruder alarm system is likely to prove more attractive, with no need for separate control panels, and the possibility, should it be desirable, for remote transmission of fire alarm signals to an alarm company monitoring centre. Such integration is not entirely without certain technical obstacles, owing to the differences between this Code and those dealing with intruder alarm systems. These will be considered in a later chapter, but they are not insurmountable; the basic philosophy should, however, be that the integrity of the fire detection and alarm arrangements should not, as a result of the integration, be reduced below the standards advocated by BS 5839-6.

The Code does not specifically refer, in the scope, to integration of fire detection with other types of alarm system, but presumably this would be equally acceptable, subject to similar safeguards to protect the integrity of the fire detection arrangements. In the very long term, we may see systems in which, for example, any permutation from the following could be provided:

- fire detection
- intruder detection
- carbon monoxide gas detection (a growth area in the UK)
- social alarm provisions.

The properties covered by the Code

Now, turning to the types of premises that come within the scope of the Code, clause 1 indicates that these include, but presumably are not restricted to, the following:

- bungalows
- multi-storey houses
- individual flats
- individual maisonettes
- mobile homes
- individual sheltered houses (and clearly flats or maisonettes)
- HMOs comprising several self-contained single-family dwelling units
- NHS 'supported living' housing in the community (e.g. for mentally ill people)
- permanently moored boats used solely as residential premises.

Individual flats, maisonettes and sheltered houses

Where I have used the word 'individual' in the above list, it should be noted that this word does not actually appear in the Code. I have used the word to emphasize that, in the case of flats, maisonettes and units of sheltered housing, the Code makes it quite clear that its recommendations only apply to the individual dwelling units and not to any communal parts. This is because, in the case of new blocks of flats, maisonettes or sheltered housing, compliance with building regulations generally necessitates that each dwelling unit is constructed as a fire resisting enclosure. The implications of this are that, in the event of a fire in, say, a single flat within a block of flats, every other flat should usually be a place of relative safety, and complete evacuation of the block will not normally be necessary, even if, when the door of the flat with the fire is opened, some smoke enters the communal escape routes. The escape routes themselves should, of course, be sterile areas, devoid of any combustible materials.

Therefore, fire detection systems are not normally installed throughout the communal areas of flats and maisonettes. Indeed, a communal fire alarm system in a block of flats can actually result in a certain amount of danger to occupants, by causing unnecessary evacuation, perhaps, in the case of an actual fire, into a smoke-filled corridor or staircase. A further practical consideration is that, unless there is a 24 hour concierge or similar arrangement, there may be no responsible person to take charge of the system, silence and reset alarms or investigate alarm conditions.

Thus, although BS 5839-6 does not specifically recommend against the installation of a fire detection and alarm system in the communal parts of flats and maisonettes (but BS 5588-1 does recommend against this in most circumstances), it excludes any such system from its scope. Most people who die from fires in blocks of flats and maisonettes do so because of a fire in their own dwelling. Avoidance of these deaths can be achieved simply by installation of smoke alarms in the flats or maisonettes (and this is what BS 5839-6 recommends in a later clause).

In the case of sheltered housing, logic might dictate that a similar situation applies, notwithstanding the more homogenously limited mobility of the occupants. Therefore, BS 5839-6 treats sheltered housing in much the same manner as other types of housing, except in respect of remote transmission of alarms, which will be discussed later. This conflicts to some extent with BS 5588-1, which singles out sheltered housing as an occupancy for which a BS 5839-1 fire detection and alarm system should be provided. However, again it should be noted that BS 5839-6 does not specifically recommend against protection of communal parts of sheltered housing, but merely excludes these areas from its scope, referring the reader to BS 5588-1 and BS 5839-1 if such protection is considered desirable.

Houses in multiple occupation

In the case of houses in multiple occupation, a different situation pertains. These properties are usually large single-family houses that have been converted for multiple occupation. (If the property were purpose built for multiple occupation in the form of numerous single-family dwelling units, it would, of course, more likely be regarded as a block of flats and not an HMO.) The integrity of fire resisting barriers may not, in practice, be such that each unit of accommodation can be treated as a place of safety. Therefore, the house must be treated as a single protected premises. Accordingly, where the Code applies to an HMO, the entire premises, and their fire detection requirements, are addressed by the Code.

However, not all HMOs come within the scope of the Code. It is often convenient to divide HMOs into two distinct categories, namely those comprising a number of self-contained dwellings and those of the hostel type. Legislation (e.g. in England and Wales, the Housing Act 1985, as amended) makes no such distinction, but such a distinction has traditionally been made in recognized technical guidance on fire precautions in HMOs (currently DoE Circular 12/92).

It was found convenient to recognize this distinction in BS 5839-6, not least because the range of premises that can be regarded as an HMO are quite wide, and the limits are not well defined. (A good lawyer can happily while away many an hour proving or disproving that a property is an HMO!) Premises that are clearly HMOs, or are normally treated (rightly or wrongly) by some authorities as HMOs, include houses sub-divided into flats, youth hostels, hostels for homeless people, homes for 'battered' women, houses shared by students, and student hostels within a university campus. Certain local authorities have even considered it appropriate to apply HMO legislation to some hotels that have been certificated under the Fire Precautions Act!

Clearly, some of the examples given above are not similar in nature to properties that we generally think of as a house; some may actually be purpose built for their present use and may never even have started life as a large single-family home. For those at one end of the range, the hostel-like properties, BS 5839-1 appears to give adequate advice on fire detection and alarm systems. Indeed, there may only be a fine dividing line between some of these premises and conventional hotels, for which BS 5839-1 is ideal. Since there is no easy line to draw between one property of the hostel type and another, BS 5839-6 excludes all HMOs of the hostel type from its scope.

However, HMOs comprising properties in which people live in self-contained single-family flats or maisonettes are within the scope of the Code. Many of these properties have some readily identifiable factors that are common to flats (e.g. the need to provide warning to occupants in the event of a fire in their own accommodation, the relatively long-term occupation by occupiers of dwelling units, the potential absence of inter-relations between occupants of different independent living units, the absence of supervision, the absence of anyone to take charge in the event of a fire warning, etc.), while retaining some factors that would also have been relevant to the original house prior to its sub-division (e.g. the need to provide warning before fire affects the communal escape routes). The likely absence of supervision, and of a responsible person to monitor the alarm system and take charge in the event of an alarm signal, alone give rise to special considerations in the design of fire detection and alarm systems. In the case of properties of this type, BS 5839-1 may not, therefore, always provide sufficient guidance.

It is appreciated that circumstances will arise in which it is not entirely clear as to whether a house should be regarded as a hostel or as a number of self-contained dwellings. This can sometimes arise in the case of certain student accommodation. However, in most cases, simple common sense will dictate which description is more appropriate and, therefore, whether the appropriate code of practice is Part 1 or Part 6 of BS 5839. In any case, the same decision process must be followed in determining which recommendations of DoE circular 12/92 in respect of, for example, means of escape should be applied; any potential difficulties of interpretation are not, therefore, unique to fire detection and alarm considerations.

In providing technical guidance, however, BS 5839-6 tends to regard houses shared by not more than six residents, living together as a single household, as equivalent to a single-family dwelling house, in that the recommendations of the Code for single-family dwellings also apply to these dwellings. A classic example of such a dwelling is one shared by students. However, even where care is provided to some of the six residents, the Code treats the premises as a dwelling (as opposed to, say, a residential care home, for which, clearly, the recommendations of BS 5839-1 would generally be more appropriate). The same approach is adopted to single-family dwellings with long-term lodgers, as research has tended to indicate that the risk to the occupants from fire is not significantly different from that in any typical single-family dwelling house.

The above interpretation of the scope of the Code is also reflected in clause 3, in which a dwelling is defined, for the purpose of interpreting BS 5839-6, as a:

> 'unit of residential accommodation occupied (whether or not as a sole or main residence):
>
> a)   by a single person or by people living together as a family; or
>
> b)   by not more than six residents living together as a single household, including a household where care is provided for residents; or

c) by persons who do not live together as a family, but who live in self-contained single-family flats, maisonettes or bedsits within the unit.'

NHS supported living in the community

The description 'NHS supported living in the community' coincides with the description in the title of a document published by the Department of Health's NHS Estates giving guidance on fire precautions in such properties. It applies to community-based premises providing 'supported living' for people who have learning difficulties or mental illness, including those with physical handicap. These properties might be regarded as akin to an HMO, but, in view of the special fire problems associated with the occupants' disabilities, it is appropriate to follow the tailor-made and detailed guidance contained in the NHS Estates document, Health Technical Memorandum 88 (HTM 88), one of the suite of documents dealing with fire safety in health care premises published under the generic title Firecode. (In fact, HTM 88 advises that, although such premises do not constitute an HMO, the standards advocated in HTM 88 would meet requirements for HMOs, imposed by local authorities.)

HTM 88 technically applies only to properties with no accommodation on a floor more than two floors above the ground or access level. HTM 88 also assumes that the premises will be occupied by no more than six residents. However, BS 5839-6 does give guidance on fire detection and alarm systems for larger properties of the same nature. The guidance in the Code on the standard of protection afforded to properties within the scope of HTM 88 is broadly consistent with the guidance in HTM 88. For properties outside the scope of HTM 88 a higher standard of system is recommended by BS 5839-6.

Mobile homes and other forms of dwelling

For the purpose of BS 5839-6, a mobile home is defined as a:

'transportable unit of living accommodation that does not meet the requirements for construction and use of road vehicles but that retains means for mobility.'

This somewhat convoluted description is based on definitions within other British Standards relevant to such accommodation.

It should be noted, however, that the Code excludes caravans from its scope. Other premises excluded from the scope include hostels and communal parts of purpose-built sheltered housing and blocks of flats or maisonettes (as already discussed), and boats (other than permanently moored boats used solely as residential premises).

Scope of protection: life and property

Most of the recommendations of the Code are concerned principally with the protection of life. However, the Code does also address property protection. This was possibly a little controversial when the first (1995) version of the Code was released for public comment. At that time, BSI requested particular comment on whether it should include recommendations for property protection. The general consensus was that it should do so. Consideration was given to pulling all such recommendations together into one section, but, in practice, this is probably not necessary, as recommendations specific only to property protection are not extensive. Moreover, for protection of large properties, the Code advocates that the fire detection and alarm installations should conform to the relevant recommendations of BS 5839-1.

Use of BS 5839-6 systems in workplaces

When the Code was first published in 1995, there was no intention that its recommendations should be applied to places of work (other than, perhaps, in the case of someone working from their home). However, without any real reference to the BSI Committee responsible for the Code, others have produced guidance on fire protection of small workplaces that makes reference to the use of BS 5839-6 systems. One such guidance document was produced by a trade association, but the more authoritative guidance document to take this approach is the 'Employers' Guide', produced by the relevant Government Departments as supporting guidance to the Fire Precautions (Workplace) Regulations 1997 (as amended).

Philosophically, there must, of course, be some very small workplaces, in which one or two interlinked smoke alarms might be satisfactory – perhaps as a means of warning to the occupants of a small, cellular office that there is a fire in an outer office, through which they must pass to escape. If the premises are so small that no electrical fire alarm system is necessary (because word of mouth would, otherwise, be a suitable means of warning in the event of fire), it might be unreasonable to expect a complete fire alarm system to be installed for the above purpose. (Even then, arguably to satisfy the Health and Safety (Safety Signs and Signals) Regulations 1996, which, effectively, require that fire alarm systems in workplaces require a standby power supply, the smoke alarm(s) would need to be mains-operated with a standby battery or capacitor.)

The problem with formal recognition of BS 5839-6 systems for use in workplaces is that it becomes something of a 'thin end of the wedge'. There is serious potential for employers to then install smoke alarms or other forms of BS 5839-6 systems as a cheap, sub-standard alternative in premises that unequivocally require a proper fire alarm system complying with BS 5839-1. (The author has even encountered the use of domestic smoke alarms in part of a large warehouse!). To avoid this situation, BS 5839-6 excludes from its scope any premises used for purposes other than as a dwelling, such as small shops, factories or similar premises used solely as a place of work. Given this exclusion with BS 5839-6, it would seem inappropriate for any other guidance document to advocate the use of BS 5839-6 systems in workplaces, or for specifications for fire detection systems in workplaces to call for compliance with BS 5839-6. It is thus the responsibility of any party proposing the use of smoke alarms, for example, to justify their use; it is likely that such applications will be very limited.

For whom is the Code intended?

When reading BS 5839-6, it is worth remembering that its recommendations, which deal with many quite complex and engineering-related matters, are not intended for the householder. Clause 1 makes clear that they are intended for architects and other building professionals, enforcing authorities, contractors and others responsible for implementing fire precautions in dwellings. However, those writing guidance for householders in the form of, say, instructions provided with smoke alarms should take account of the Code's recommendations (particularly clause 24 which deals with user instructions) in their guidance. There will still, of course, be a need for documents such as the Government's 'Smoke Alarms in the Home', which give simple guidance to householders. It may be necessary, nevertheless, for such documents to be updated to take account of the Code's recommendations.

4. Format and contents of the Code

The 2004 version of BS 5839-6 is set out in '*practice specification*' format. In this format, each clause begins with a 'Commentary', followed by the actual recommendations themselves. To distinguish between the commentary and the recommendations, the commentary is written in italics, while the recommendations are written in normal standard Roman text.

The purpose of the commentary is to provide background information on the principles associated with the topic that is the subject matter of the clause in question. It is written in something of a narrative style and contains no specific or positive recommendations. Thus, for example, to avoid confusion, the word 'should' is not used in the commentary, as this verb is reserved for the recommendations; rather, the wording used contains phrases such as 'it needs to be ensured', 'it is appropriate', etc.

For the contractor who wishes, simply, to comply with the recommendations of the Code and is not concerned with the whys and wherefores of the underlying philosophy, there should be absolutely no need to read any of the commentary. Similarly, if anybody, such as an enforcing authority, third-party certification body or representative of the user or purchaser, is carrying out an audit of compliance with the Code, the audit should only be against the recommendations of the Code and not the commentary. In this sense, compliance with the commentary does not arise.

The commentary is, however, useful for those who want a greater insight into the recommendations. Such insight might actually be necessary in situations in which strict compliance with the recommendations is difficult, but there is a desire to still meet the spirit of the recommendations. Thus, in considering whether a 'variation' from the recommendations of the Code is acceptable, reference may need to be made to the commentary. ('Variations' were described as 'deviations' in the 1995 version of the Code.)

Turning to the recommendations themselves, these are relatively short in the 2004 Code and, for ease of reference, each and every recommendation is numbered. This assists those who wish to create checklists for compliance with the Code and to refer to a specific recommendation when highlighting any area of non-compliance.

Unlike BS 5839-1, which is sub-divided into seven sections that 'overlay' the conventional sub-division into clauses, BS 5839-6 is simply divided into 26 clauses, with six supporting annexes. Some clauses cover matters that warrant an entire section of BS 5839-1, reflecting the simpler nature of the systems generally installed in dwellings. A contrast may also be drawn with BS 5839-1, in that different sections in that Code are intended for different parties, such as the designer, the installer, etc. However, it is likely that the entire readership for whom BS 5839-6 is intended should probably read virtually all clauses that apply to the Category and Grade of system, and to the property with which they are concerned. This is because, for many BS 5839-6 systems, the designer, installer and commissioning organization will be the same party.

In the following paragraphs, each clause and annex is reviewed and important aspects that will be discussed in later chapters of this guide are highlighted.

I Scope

The scope of the Code was discussed at length in the previous chapter. As noted in that chapter, clause 1 describes the types of property for which recommendations are provided and the types of fire detection system covered. This clause also outlines the types of property that are outside the scope of the Code. The intended readership of the Code is defined, as is the scope of protection for which recommendations are given, namely property protection as well as life safety.

2 Normative references

The various other publications to which BS 5839-6 refers can be sub-divided into two groups, namely 'Normative' references and 'Bibliography'. The latter is discussed at the end of this chapter. 'Normative' references are basically other standards and codes that provide requirements or recommendations that should be followed. Failure to comply with a normative reference is equivalent to failure to comply with BS 5839-6, since normative references, in effect, form part of the Code. All except one of these are, in this case, BSI publications.

The normative references incorporated within the Code are set out in clause 2. If the normative reference includes a date, only the edition of that date applies. If the reference is undated in the Code, the latest edition of the document applies, together with any amendments.

Since most normative references in the Code are undated, this means that, over a period of time, the recommendations of BS 5839-6 could change subtly, because of changes to the recommendations or requirements contained in normative references. It is, therefore, important that users of the Code ensure that they refer to the latest version of undated normative references.

3 Definitions

Clause 3 defines the meanings of 35 terms used in BS 5839-6, *as they are to be understood for the purpose of interpreting the Code*. Perhaps the most important is the definition of dwelling since this helps define the scope of the Code; this has already been discussed in the previous chapter.

In many cases, the definitions used are those contained in British Standards or other codes, so ensuring consistency. Where this is not the case, and the definition given is unique to BS 5839-6, significant differences between the BS 5839-6 definition and that in other codes are highlighted.

This occurs, for example, in the case of the definition of monitored wiring. For the purpose of BS 5839-6, monitored wiring is generally wiring in which an open circuit results in a fault warning, whereas a short circuit results in *either* a fault warning or a fire warning. This contrasts with the definition given in BS 5839-1, which is such that, in monitored wiring, a fault warning (and not a fire warning) results from both open and short circuit faults; monitoring, as defined in BS 5839-1 is, in fact, recommended for some systems in BS 5839-6. (If this appears to be confusing, all should become clear in later parts of the Code and this guide!)

Most of the definitions merely formalize the common understanding of the terms in question, and they will be familiar to most users of the Code. However, a small number of definitions determine in some subtle but important manner the way in which the Code is to be understood. One example, the definition of monitored wiring, has already been discussed.

Perhaps the most significantly subtle of the other definitions is the definition of fire risk. There is a tendency for the terms risk and hazard to be used, quite incorrectly, in fire protection as though they are synonymous. The ubiquitous 'fire risk assessment' that modern fire safety legislation requires also often highlights the fact that different people mean different things when they talk about 'fire risk' – hardly helpful if we are to communicate successfully with each other on matters pertaining to avoidance, or assessment, of fire risk. BS 5839-6 makes it clear that, for the purpose of this document, fire risk is to be understood as a combination of the probability of fire occurring (which, by itself, is often incorrectly referred to as 'fire risk') and the magnitude of the consequences of fire. This tends to be consistent with the understanding of the term 'risk' used by those in the health and safety field, where the terms hazard and risk are used less interchangeably.

Thus, for example, by the definition in BS 5839-6, the fire risk would be low if there were very little chance of an outbreak of fire, even though the probability and extent of harm to occupants in the event of fire might not be low. On the other hand, even if the probability and extent of potential harm were quite low, say because of good means of escape, the fire risk would, by definition, be high if one of the occupants were known to be prone to wilful fire raising.

An important new definition in the 2004 version of BS 5839-6 is that given for the term 'principal habitable room'. The importance of the term is that, for example, in new dwellings, the Code recommends the installation of a heat detector in this room. In practice, in most dwellings, the room will be the room that is easily recognizable as the 'living room'.

Other important definitions, first introduced in the 2004 version of the Code include those applicable to the four categories of false alarm identified in the Code. (The term 'false alarm' itself is also defined.) The term 'mixed system', first introduced in the 1995 version of the Code, is also formally defined for the first time in the 2004 version.

4 Fire risk assessment

This clause of the Code effectively sets out the philosophy that underpins a substantial part of the Code. The clause is supported by an Annex, which describes a 'first principles' approach to determining the appropriate form of fire detection and alarm system and the appropriate level of protection. This thereby not only offers justification for the recommendations made in later clauses dealing with these matters, but also provides an approach that can be used if the reader wants to tailor-make protection for a particular dwelling instead of adopting later recommendations for 'typical' dwellings. Both protection of life and protection of property are addressed, with particular emphasis, of course, on the former.

Such is the importance of this clause that a later chapter of this guide is dedicated to its subject matter. However, at this stage, it should be noted that the clause advises that the level of fire risk in dwellings covered by the Code is unlikely to be sufficiently low to obviate the need for some form of fire detection and alarm system. Equally, the clause acknowledges the need for generic prescription of design parameters for specific forms of dwelling, for use when factors such as occupant characteristics are unknown. This will very often be the case, particularly in the case of application of the Code to new dwellings in order to satisfy building regulations.

5 System components

Effectively, this short clause simply lists the relevant product standards with which components of the system should conform. In most cases, the relevant product standards are British Standards; in the case of the more sophisticated systems, these will be the British version of European Standards, published as the relevant part of BS EN 54.

6 Monitoring of circuits

This clause does not apply to smoke alarms, but only to fire alarm systems that incorporate control equipment. The clause provides recommendations for the monitoring of power supplies and circuits external to any control equipment.

7 Grades of system

This clause formally defines six 'Grades' of system. System Grade is related to engineering considerations and system format, as opposed to the level of protection afforded by the system, which is addressed in the next clause. The Grades of system are discussed in the next chapter of this guide.

8 Categories of system

Clause 8 provides a method for specifying different levels of protection by reference to five 'Categories' of system defined in this clause (in the same way that eight Categories of system are defined by BS 5839-1). Three system Categories are intended for protection of life, while a further two are intended for protection of property. Again, this is very similar to, but simpler than, the system sub-divisions contained in BS 5839-1.

9 Choice of system

Having described a basis for risk assessment and its implications for system design, and set out a menu of system Grades and Categories, the Code logically goes on to provide definitive advice on the Grades and Categories of system that are appropriate for different types and sizes of dwelling. This enables the reader to by-pass the fire risk assessment clause, particularly if the occupant characteristics, which should be taken into account in a risk assessment, are unknown. (For those familiar with emergency lighting and BS 5266-1, there is some analogy between this clause and the system choice clause in that Code.)

This clause is one of the most important in the entire Code, since it contains, within a single, quite complex table, the generic 'standard' solution for fire detection in any particular type of dwelling.

10 Types of fire detector and their selection

This clause reviews the 'armoury' of detector types available to the designer and specifier. Methods of operation of the detectors are described, and there is guidance on the applications for which each type of detector is suitable. The latter guidance is related not only to fire type but system Category (as defined in clause 8).

11 Location and siting of fire detectors

Clause 11 provides further guidance on the location and siting of fire detectors. To a large extent, this will be related to system Category, since system Category will basically define the number of detectors that need to be provided and their location. However, detailed recommendations on detector siting and spacing are also given.

12 Limitation of false alarms

This is a very lengthy clause, particularly in comparison to the short clause contained in the 1995 version of the Code. This reflects the much greater importance now attached to the avoidance of false alarms. Pragmatic guidance on avoidance of false alarms is provided. Emphasis is placed on selection of the correct type of detector and facilities for user control. The automatic transmission of fire signals to the fire service is discouraged unless significant attention is given to avoidance of false alarms.

13 Audible fire alarm devices and audibility

This clause describes a number of considerations in respect of sounder type and frequency. The most important recommendations of the clause, however, are those dealing with audibility. Definitive advice is given on the sound levels that should be achieved at the bedrooms of the dwelling.

14 Fire alarm warnings for deaf and hard of hearing people

This is an important new clause in the 2004 version of BS 5839-6, which reflects the greater importance that is, happily, now attached, more generally, to fire safety of disabled people. The clause provides very useful guidance on the arrangements that should be made to warn deaf people, and people who are hard of hearing, in the event of fire. In general, the use of 'hearing impaired fire alarm kits', complying with BS 5446-3: 2004, is recommended, unless a more sophisticated fire detection and alarm system is installed, in which case reference is made to the relevant recommendations of BS 5839-1.

15 Power supplies

Clause 15 provides detailed guidance on the power supplies (normal and, where relevant, standby) that should be used with each of the six Grades of system. Clause 9 recommends that, for many applications, systems should have a standby power supply, and the appropriate specification for a standby supply is given in clause 15.

16 Wiring

Recommendations are given for the type of wiring that should be used for each of the six Grades of system. As well as electrical characteristics, protection against fire and mechanical damage are considered to the extent appropriate. The Code accepts, however, that 'wireless' systems may be used, and these are considered in a later clause (see below).

17 Control and indicating equipment

This clause does not apply, of course, to systems comprising only smoke alarms, unless these are connected to some form of central power supply/

control unit. However, since more complex ('Grades' of) system are considered in the Code, clause 17 provides recommendations for the siting of any associated control equipment and for the facilities that should be provided by such equipment.

18 Manual call points

Discussion of manual call points is also relevant only to systems in very large properties. Guidance on the properties in which manual call points should be installed is given in this clause. Where these are to be provided, the clause provides recommendations on matters such as method of operation and siting.

19 Zoning and other means for identification of the source of alarm conditions

Yet another clause that is only relevant to very large properties, in which a system of the type considered in BS 5839-1 is appropriate. Nevertheless, the very broad scope of the Code makes this clause necessary for these large properties, in which detection zone indication will be valuable. However, in the case of an HMO, other means of determining the source of an alarm condition are recognized and discussed.

20 Remote transmission of alarm signals

The circumstances under which this facility might be relevant are discussed, along with a number of technical issues relevant to transmission of alarms to (ultimately) the fire service. The clause tends to discourage the provision of such a facility unless there is a need for it and/or there are stringent precautions to avoid the unnecessary summoning of the fire service.

21 Radio-linked systems

This clause deals with the special considerations applicable to systems that use radio links between components, principally control equipment and detectors or sounders. Recommendations for power supplies are given, along with advice on factors relevant to the application of such systems.

22 Electromagnetic compatibility

Detailed guidance on this subject would be out of place in this Code. In the case of systems of the type to which BS 5839-1 applies, the Code refers to the more detailed recommendations contained in that Code.

23 Installation, commissioning and certification

Basic good installation practices are described in this clause. In addition, there are recommendations in respect of final commissioning and certification, using the model certificates contained in Annexes to the Code.

24 User instructions

This clause defines the information that the supplier should provide to the occupier or owner of the property. The recommended information is quite comprehensive and should prove of value in ensuring that systems are operated and maintained correctly. The clause is, therefore, quite important, and, in effect, defines the minimum information that should even, for example, be provided by manufacturers of smoke alarms.

25 Routine testing

This clause follows on to some extent from the previous clause in that, although the user will not have a copy of BS 5839-6, the guidance in this clause should be incorporated in the instructions described in the previous clause.

26 Maintenance

This short clause briefly advises on the form of servicing that should be adopted and the periods between each servicing routine.

Annex A Fire risk assessment for dwellings

This is an informative annex that is intended to assist in determination of the appropriate Grade and Category of system, according to the nature of the fire risk in a particular dwelling. Guidance is given on the implications of a number of factors for system design, if a designer were endeavouring to 'tailor-make' a system for a specific dwelling. The factors comprise the actual objective of the system, the characteristics of the occupants, lifestyle factors and ignition sources. Additional factors are given in the case of systems that are also intended to protect the property, as opposed to purely the occupants.

As the annex is informative, it is not necessary to refer to it in order to comply with BS 5839-6. However, it is a useful basis for the pragmatic assessment of fire risk in any dwelling.

Annex B Choice of appropriate Grade of fire detection and fire alarm system

This, again, is an informative annex. It basically sets out the pros and cons of the six Grades of system defined in clause 7 of the Code. In conjunction with Annex A, it can, therefore, assist the specifier in deciding on the appropriate Grade of system in certain circumstances.

Annex C Control and indicating equipment for Grade B systems

This normative annex is somewhat unusual in that it is, in effect, a mini equipment standard within a code of practice. It sets out functional requirements for a simple domestic fire alarm control panel. It is unfortunate that, in practice, there is no demand for such a control panel (and hence, little, if any, availability of such equipment) as it would be inexpensive, but offer greater sophistication than a system comprising only smoke alarms.

Annex D Model guidance to occupiers and landlords regarding avoidance of false alarms in systems with facilities for automatic transmission of fire signals to the fire and rescue service

This annex provides guidance to occupiers and landlords, which should be read before signals from a domestic fire detection and alarm system are transmitted automatically to the fire service. It is a specific recommendation of clause 20 of the Code that, before any facility for automatic transmission of fire signals to the fire service becomes operative, confirmation is obtained from the occupier or landlord (as appropriate) that the guidance has been received and read. Clause 20 also recommends that this guidance is sent to the occupier or landlord at least every 12 months.

Annex E Model certificates for Grade A systems

This annex contains separate suitable certificates for certifying that a fire detection and alarm system has indeed been designed, installed, commissioned and accepted in accordance with the recommendations of the Code for a Grade A system.

Annex F Model certificate for Grades B, C, D, E and F systems

This single certificate of design, installation and commissioning is much simpler than the three equivalent certificates contained in Annex E, reflecting the greater simplicity of the systems and the greater likelihood that design, installation and commissioning will be undertaken by a single party. However, should different parties be responsible for each of the three processes, the certificate can be amended to indicate the actual process for which the signatory is responsible.

Bibliography

A number of documents to which the Code makes reference, but not necessary for compliance with the Code, are set out in a bibliography at the end of the Code.

5. Recognized forms of fire detection: Grades of system

If we were to review all the fire detection products that are, or may be, used for the protection of dwellings, we would end up with a surprisingly wide range of permutations of system. The Code recognizes all of these forms of fire detection. After all, a British Standard code of practice is meant to do just that – set out good practice in respect of the equipment that is on offer in the marketplace. Indeed, to a limited extent, the Code even attempts to anticipate some variations that might be offered in the future, so hopefully avoiding unnecessary obstacles to developments in technology.

It was noted in an earlier chapter that the scope of the Code encompasses fire detection and alarm 'systems' ranging from a single battery-operated smoke alarm to a sophisticated analogue/addressable automatic fire detection and alarm system. However, this does not imply that all of these various forms of fire detection are suitable for all applications. In order to specify the appropriate form of fire detection for any application, the Code defines six different 'Grades' of system, designated Grade A (the most sophisticated) to Grade F (the simplest).

The six Grades are defined as follows:

Grade A: A fire detection and fire alarm system, which incorporates
             control and indicating equipment conforming to BS EN 54-2
             and power supply equipment conforming to BS EN 54-4,
             and which is designed and installed in accordance with all the
             recommendations of sections 1 to 4 inclusive of BS 5839-1,
             except those in the following clauses, for which the
             corresponding clauses of BS 5839-6 should be substituted.

Clause/sub-clause of BS 5839-1	Corresponding clause/sub-clause of BS 5839-6
16 (Audible alarm signals)	13 (Audible fire alarm devices and audibility)
18 (Fire alarm warnings for people with impaired hearing)	14 (Fire alarm warnings for deaf and hard of hearing people)
20 (Manual call points)	18 (Manual call points)
25.4 e) (Capacity of standby batteries)	15.2 c) (Capacity of standby batteries)
27 (Radio-linked systems)	21 (Radio-linked systems)

Grade B: A fire detection and fire alarm system comprising fire detectors (other than smoke alarms and heat alarms), fire alarm sounders, and control and indicating equipment that either conforms to BS EN 54-2 (and power supply complying with BS EN 54-4) or to Annex C of BS 5839-6.

Grade C: A system of fire detectors and alarm sounders (which may be combined in the form of smoke alarms) connected to a common power supply, comprising the normal mains and a standby supply, with central control equipment.

Grade D: A system of one or more mains-powered smoke alarms, each with an integral standby supply. (The system may, in addition, incorporate one or more mains-powered heat alarms, each with an integral standby supply.)

Grade E: A system of one or more mains-powered smoke alarms with no standby supply. (The system may, in addition, incorporate one or more heat alarms, with or without standby supplies.)

Grade F: A system of one or more battery-powered smoke alarms. (The system may, in addition, also incorporate one or more battery-powered heat alarms.)

The first and most important point to note about the Grades is that they have, quite intentionally and very carefully, been defined in a form of descending order of sophistication; as we ascend through the Grades from Grade F to Grade A, each time we go up a Grade we improve one or more of the following in some way:

- The reliability of the system (e.g. by adding a standby power supply when we go from Grade E to Grade D).
- The likelihood that the system will be working, and not faulty, when it is required to operate (i.e. high 'availability'). This does not just

depend on having 'reliable' equipment, as even the most reliable equipment and wiring may develop a fault that disables the system at some time during its life; monitoring (which is enhanced as we go from, say, Grade D to Grade C) improves availability as it gives us an immediate warning when a fault disables the system, enabling early repair and so reducing the down time for which the system would be disabled pending discovery of the fault during routine testing or servicing.

• The degree of control over the system (e.g. by adding some form of control equipment as we go from Grade D to Grade C).

Because of the greater degree of sophistication as we ascend the Grades, a higher Grade of system will normally involve greater expenditure, which may be unnecessary and not cost effective if the fire risk is already low. For example, if advising the single, young and fit occupant of an existing two-bedroom bungalow on the appropriate form of fire detection, it might be judged that a single battery-operated smoke alarm would be sufficient.

True, the occupant may not replace the battery at the end of its life or may have removed the battery when exasperated by false alarms. However, the probability that the occupant will die in a fire is already quite low. The probability of fire occurring when the battery is removed, with the consequent death of the occupant, is probably sufficiently low to be acceptable. It would certainly be unreasonable to expect the occupant to install a fire detection and alarm system complying with BS 5839-1! The matter of fire risk assessment and system choice are considered in other clauses of the Code and will therefore be discussed in later chapters.

Enforcing authorities generally have a need to specify only the minimum acceptable Grade of system. But in so doing, it is important that they do not, perhaps inadvertently, preclude people from installing something better. This has tended to be the situation under building regulations, whereby, in new dwellings (other than very large dwellings), the builder has the choice of installing mains-operated smoke alarms (with or without a standby power supply) or a full BS 5839-1 system. This left no scope for anything in between the two.

For example, a combined fire/intruder detection system might well afford a 'better' standard than a number of interconnected smoke alarms, but would not necessarily comply with all the recommendations of BS 5839-1; indeed, such an 'integrated' system would be outside the scope of BS 5839-1, but would be recognized as a Grade C system under BS 5839-6. A fire detection system with control equipment somewhat simpler than that required by BS EN 54-2 might well provide a very good standard of protection, but would not comply with BS 5839-1, which recommends that control equipment conform to BS EN 54-2. However, such a system could be recognized as a Grade B system under BS 5839-6.

In future, the Government Departments responsible for building regulations (if they accept BS 5839-6, which seems very likely) need only specify a Grade D system for normal-sized dwellings, rather than, as at present, including rudimentary design recommendations, which fall short of compliance with BS 5839-6, in the guidance that supports building regulations. Because it is an inherent feature of the Grades that any requirement for one Grade of system can automatically be satisfied by the installation of a higher Grade of system, the builder would be free to choose to install a Grade A, B, or C system, instead of the Grade D system specified.

Not all clauses of BS 5839-6 apply to every Grade of system. When we come to consider matters such as power supplies, wiring, etc. we will find that different recommendations apply to different Grades of system. Firstly, however, let us examine more closely the six Grades of system in our fire detection armoury.

Grade A systems

Basically, as is clear from the definition, these, to all intents and purposes, are BS 5839-1 systems, with, possibly, one or two variations from the recommendations of that code of practice. Before sending the reader off to read BS 5839-1, however, the Code makes five caveats in respect of the use of Part 1.

By far the most important of the recommended exceptions to the advice in BS 5839-1 relates to alarm audibility. The Code advocates that, for Grade A systems, the advice contained in clause 13 of BS 5839-6 be substituted for the recommendations of BS 5839-1 on audibility (as set out in clause 16 of Part 1). Alarm audibility will be discussed in some detail in a later chapter of this Guide. At this stage, we may note that compliance with the recommendations of BS 5839-1 would necessitate, in many cases, an alarm sounder in every bedroom, and a significantly larger number of sounders throughout, say, a large mansion than are often provided in practice. However, for HMOs, the Code still enables the enforcing authority to determine whether the recommendation of BS 5839-1, that a sound pressure level of 75 dB(A) should be achieved at the bedhead in bedrooms, should be satisfied, necessitating a sounder in each bedroom.

Also, if, in a Grade A system, there is a need for special facilities to warn deaf people, or people who are hard of hearing, in the event of fire, BS 5839-6 recommends that, rather than following the recommendations of BS 5839-1 for such facilities, the recommendations of clause 14 of BS 5839-6 be adopted. This is to avoid unnecessarily sophisticated and expensive systems in the case of domestic applications.

Most dwellings do not need the provision of manual call points. Thus, even in a Grade A system, the recommendations of BS 5839-1 for manual call points would be inappropriate. However, the possible need for manual call points, and recommendations relating to their provision, are the subject of clause 18 of BS 5839-6, which, in a Grade A system, should be adopted instead of the corresponding clause of BS 5839-1.

Clause 25.4 e) of BS 5839-1 makes recommendations for the duration of the standby (battery) supply that should be provided. It is considered that these recommendations do not translate well to domestic premises, and BS 5839-6 recommends that the guidance in clause 15.2 c) of the Code be used instead. The recommendations of Part 6 are actually more onerous than those of Part 1, in terms of the standby duration required. Whereas BS 5839-1 recommends that the standby duration for a system intended to protect life should be 24 hours (reduced to six hours if an automatically started standby generator is provided), the minimum standby duration recommended by BS 5839-6 is 72 hours.

The final substitution of Part 6 recommendations for Part 1 recommendations concerns radio-linked systems. Part 6 points out the potential disadvantages of batteries as the power supply for radio-linked components in dwellings, albeit that the potential advantages of radio-linked systems are also recognized. Although, as a minimum, the recommendations of the relevant clause of BS 5839-1 are applicable in a Grade A system, additional recommendations regarding the use of 'long life' batteries apply to Grade A radio-linked systems in houses in multiple occupation.

Grade B systems

Grade B systems are similar to Grade A systems, in that they do not incorporate smoke alarms. They comprise dedicated control and indicating equipment, fire alarm sounders and fire detectors. The control and indicating equipment may (and probably will) conform to BS EN 54-2, and so be identical to that used in Grade A systems. In this case, the actual hardware installed in both the Grade A and the Grade B system will be identical; the difference between the two systems will then be only minor relaxations for the Grade B system in respect of a small number of recommendations that apply to Grade A systems.

However, by definition, the control and indicating equipment in a Grade B system does not need to conform to BS EN 54-2. It is this aspect that, in practice, is most likely to differentiate between the two Grades of system, if manufacturers decide to produce control panels that conform to the Annex of BS 5839-6. Control equipment for Grade B systems is considered in a later chapter. At this stage, we need note only that it is simpler in nature than that specified in BS EN 54-2 and that it is not required to satisfy the onerous environmental tests in that standard.

Grade C systems

Grade C systems fill a gap between systems comprising interconnected smoke alarms and fire detection and alarm systems of the type addressed by BS 5839-1. The two important criteria for a Grade C system are a central power supply (mains and standby) for the fire detectors and sounders (which may be combined in the form of smoke alarms), associated with which there is central control equipment.

Annex B of the Code gives two examples of such systems, namely:

a) One or more smoke alarms and heat alarms operating at extra-low voltage and connected to a control unit; such control units are available.

b) Intruder alarm systems or social alarm systems that incorporate control and indicating equipment to which one or more fire detectors are connected; these detectors could, again, be smoke alarms, but may simply be conventional fire detectors in which case there will also be independent alarm sounders.

Again, such 'integrated' systems already exist. However, the recommendations of the Code take precedence over any conflicting recommendations of other relevant codes, such as those for the intruder alarm system, social alarm system, etc. As discussed in an earlier chapter, there is probably greater scope for the future use of integrated systems complying with the recommendations for Grade C systems.

The Code recommends that wiring is monitored, although this recommendation would be satisfied if a fire signal, rather than a fault signal, were given in the event of an open circuit or short circuit fault in wiring. This may well be the case in some integrated fire/intruder systems.

Grades D, E, and F systems

These three Grades comprise smoke alarms, and can also incorporate heat alarms. With a few exceptions, recommendations of the Code in respect of them merely set out what has already become recognized good practice.

An important recommendation is, however, that, where more than one smoke alarm or heat alarm is installed, the smoke alarms and heat alarms (if provided) should be interlinked. In particular, the Code recommends that this should certainly be the case in new dwellings and certain existing dwellings, including most HMOs, rented properties of two or more storeys and all houses of three or more storeys. It is also the ideal situation in other dwellings.

6. Recognized levels of protection: Categories of system

Clause 8 of the Code defines five different 'Categories' of system, offering different levels of protection. Those with experience of BS 5839-1 will be very familiar with this concept, which is fundamental to the application of Part 1. In the case of Part 1, the designations L1, L2, L3, L4, L5, P1 and P2 are used to describe the seven Categories of automatic fire detection and alarm system defined in that Code; Category L systems are intended for protection of life, and Category P are intended for protection of property.

In the case of Part 6, the analogous system Categories are given the designations LD1, LD2, LD3, PD1 and PD2, the letter D denoting a Part 6 system installed in a dwelling. Just as it means absolutely nothing for a specification to require compliance with BS 5839-1, without reference to system Category, it means very little to require compliance with BS 5839-6, without specifying the Category (and indeed Grade) of system required. (However, as we shall see in the next chapter, Part 6 does provide some guidance as to the circumstances in which different Categories of system may be appropriate.)

The Code defines the five Categories of system in the manner described below:

Category LD systems are intended to protect life, and are sub-divided into:

Category LD1:   A system installed throughout the dwelling, incorporating detectors in all circulation spaces that form part of the escape routes from the dwelling, and in all rooms and areas in which fire might start, other than toilets, bathrooms and shower rooms. (This is more or less identical to the level of protection afforded by a BS 5839-1 Category L1 system.)

Category LD2:   A system incorporating detectors in all circulation spaces that form part of the escape routes from the dwelling, and in all rooms or areas that present a high fire risk to occupants; the concept of 'fire risk' is well explained in the Code, and is consequently discussed in a later chapter of this Guide. (Again, the concept is very similar to a Category L2 system under Part 1, in that LD2 incorporates, but extends, LD3, just as L2 under Part 1 incorporates, and extends, an L3 system; but note the distinction between L3 and LD3 highlighted below.)

Category LD3:   A system incorporating detectors in all circulation spaces that form part of the escape routes from the dwelling. Note that, in a Category LD3 system, the detectors are located only in the escape routes. This contrasts with the Category L3 systems defined in BS 5839-1, which include detectors in rooms adjoining escape routes as well as within the actual escape routes themselves.

Category PD systems are intended to protect property, and are sub-divided into:

Category PD1:   A system installed throughout the dwelling, incorporating detectors in all rooms and areas in which fire might start, other than toilets, bathrooms and shower rooms.

Category PD2:   A system incorporating detectors only in defined rooms or areas of the dwelling in which the risk of fire to property is judged to warrant their provision.

These definitions are very much in accordance with those for Category P1 and P2 systems in BS 5839-1.

In practice, while, in industrial and commercial buildings, it is not uncommon to find automatic fire detection systems installed solely for the protection of property, it will be very rare to find an automatic fire detection system installed in a dwelling purely for property protection. Indeed, such a system could be regarded as non-compliant with the Code, which recommends that all dwellings should be protected to at least the standard afforded by a Category LD3 system. (The Category PD system might not satisfy the recommendations of the Code on audibility in a Category LD3 system; this is discussed in a later chapter.) Exceptions may, however, occur, but will be very unusual indeed. For example, the Code gives the example of a house of historic importance in which no one sleeps; the sole objective of the fire detection just might then be only protection of property.

Normally, therefore, PD systems will be designed to comply with the recommendations for a Category LD system; the result is a combined PD/LD system. The recommendations for the two Categories of system may differ. For example, in a Category PD system, the most important objective is to summon the fire brigade, usually via a link to an alarm receiving centre. This is not usually necessary in a Category LD system. The alarm signal in a Category PD system need not necessarily be audible in all bedrooms in a large mansion. However, in an LD3 system, alarm audibility would be extremely important. Where a combined LD/PD system is installed, the Code, not surprisingly, recommends simply that the system should comply with the recommendations for each of the Categories of system.

In the following two chapters of this Guide, we will consider the factors that govern the choice of system Category. However, we should first examine the defined system Categories in a little more detail, in order to achieve a good understanding of the protection philosophy applicable to each Category of system.

LD1 systems

The philosophy in the case of these systems is quite simple. There is full coverage throughout all parts of the dwelling other than toilets, bathrooms and shower rooms. The latter are excluded because of the low probability of ignition, low fire load and, in the case of bathrooms and shower rooms, the somewhat hostile environment. The objective is to give the earliest practicable warning, regardless of where fire starts. In some areas of the dwelling (but not circulation areas), heat detectors could be used to achieve this objective. Note that, in referring to all 'areas' in which fire might start, the Code includes loft spaces.

The LD1 level of protection is, therefore, quite onerous. If, nevertheless, on the basis of a commonsense risk assessment, it is considered that, although a very high standard of protection is warranted, protection of just one area may be somewhat 'over the top', it is still possible to regard the system as Category LD1 with an agreed variation, which should then be recorded on the installation certificate. Alternatively, what amounts to the same thing, the system could be regarded as Category LD2; a rose by any other name!

LD2 systems

Although these systems may still offer a high standard of protection, fire detection is only provided within the circulation areas (in accordance with the recommendations for a Category LD3 system) and in rooms or areas of the dwelling that present a high fire risk to occupants. Note that the risk might be to occupants of the room or to occupants of other rooms. An example of an LD2 system, recommended by the Code for a typical new two-storey dwelling, is one with smoke alarms in the downstairs hallway and upstairs landing, plus heat alarms in the lounge and kitchen (see Chapter 9).

From the point of view of a contractor who has to comply with a specification that requires a Category LD2 system, it will normally be the responsibility of the specifier to define where the 'extra' detection (i.e. over and above that in the circulation areas) is to be provided. From the point of view of the specifier or system designer, it may be necessary to carefully assess the risk, unless the intent is to comply with generic requirements, perhaps imposed by an enforcing authority, or with generic recommendations of the Code (e.g. for heat detection to be provided in the living room and kitchen of a new two-storey house).

The matter of risk assessment is discussed later in this Guide. At this stage, we should, however, take note of three points. Firstly, 'fire risk' does not take only the probability of ignition into account, but also the possible consequences of a fire. A Category LD2 system may, therefore, be appropriate because, for example, occupants are disabled and would find it difficult to escape in the event of fire, even though the probability of fire is no greater than that in an 'average' dwelling. Secondly, as discussed above, the Code does, in some cases, make specific recommendations as to which 'additional' areas should be protected in a Category LD2 system, and it should be noted that the 'additional' detectors need not necessarily be smoke detectors.

LD3 systems

These systems offer the basic minimum level of protection that should be provided in all homes. The objective is only to give a warning before heat or smoke from a fire anywhere in the property makes use of the escape routes impossible. It is important to understand that the system is not intended to protect anyone in the room of fire origin; moreover, if the door of that room is closed, the time available for escape after a Category LD3 system operates could be quite short.

Only smoke detectors can be used in a Category LD3 system, as heat detectors would be too slow to operate, and the objective defined above would not be satisfied. (However, if, in a large house, a Grade A system were warranted, detectors would be sited in accordance with the relevant recommendations of BS 5839-1, which, for the protection of escape routes, recommends detectors in rooms adjoining escape routes; these could, of course, be heat detectors.)

PD1 systems

Although, in order to be as comprehensive as possible, the Code does consider property protection, we shall see later that, when protection of a very large house of three or more storeys, such as a country mansion, is required, the Code simply recommends compliance with the recommendations of BS 5839-1 for a Category P1 system.

Properties of more limited size may, however, be protected in accordance with the recommendations of BS 5839-6 for a Category PD1 system. The siting of detectors will be very similar to that in the case of a Category LD1 system. Although toilets, bathrooms and shower rooms need not be protected, detection is normally required in all other areas. However, the Code does advise that, exceptionally, even in a Category PD1 system, it may be acceptable to omit detectors from areas in which there is no combustible material and no source of ignition. The example given in the Code is a disused cellar or attic in which all electricity supplies are permanently disconnected.

PD2 systems

These systems offer 'partial protection' and incorporate detectors only in those parts of the building in which there is significant potential for ignition or where a fire could present a high risk to property or contents. Within these protected areas, of course, siting and spacing of detectors are the same as in a Category PD1 (or LD1) system.

A common misconception in the protection of properties with high value contents, such as works of art, antique furniture, etc., is that a partial protection system should include detection only in the areas that have the items of value. In fact, the probability of fire in these areas is often quite low, and the real threat comes from spread of fire from other areas. Because of this, the Code recommends that, in a PD2 system, detectors should be installed in areas where ignition sources or readily ignitable materials are present, where fire could spread rapidly or where supervision is absent, as well as areas in which a fire could rapidly result in high loss. It is also recommended that protected areas are separated from unprotected areas by fire resisting construction.

7. System selection: Choosing the appropriate Grade and Category of system

Clearly, bearing in mind that there are six Grades and five Categories of system, the number of permutations of Grade and Category is extensive, and, at first sight, a daunting menu is available to the specifier. In practice, not all possible permutations can occur; for example, it is hardly likely that anyone would use interlinked battery-operated smoke alarms for a Category P1 system!

More fundamentally, recognition of the various Grades and Categories of system is not intended to imply that simply any Grade or Category of system is suitable for every application. We have, for example, already seen that, in order to satisfy the recommendations of the Code, even a relatively small new dwelling will normally need to be provided with one or more mains-operated smoke alarms with a standby supply. This immediately eliminates Grade E and Grade F systems for new dwellings.

If we study the Code carefully, we may take the view that, in effect, it enables us to arrive at the correct choice of system by two quite different routes. The two routes to selection of the appropriate Grade and Category of system for any particular application could possibly be described as:

(i)   the 'first principles' risk assessment approach; and
(ii) the prescriptive 'pre-determined' approach.

In the first case, the recommendations of clause 4 ('Fire risk assessment'), supported by Annex A ('Fire risk assessment for dwellings') and Annex B ('Choice of appropriate Grade of fire detection and fire alarm system') can be used as a basis for deciding on where to install detectors and what Grade of system would be appropriate.

However, for users of the Code who wish more definitive advice, clause 9 of the Code ('Choice of system') gives specific advice, by reference to Grade and Category of system, on how to protect typical dwellings. The guidance in clause 9 is, of course, based entirely on the considerations described in clause 4, Annex A and Annex B.

In the following two chapters, both methods of system selection are described. Even if the prescriptive approach is adopted, it is useful to understand the fundamental considerations on which the definitive guidance in the Code is based. These fundamental considerations are discussed in the next chapter.

8. System selection: The first principles ('Fire risk assessment') approach

Level of protection

Clause 4 of the Code ('Fire risk assessment'), in conjunction with Annex A ('Fire risk assessment for dwellings'), is perhaps the most important in the entire Code. There are a number of reasons for this.

Firstly, this clause and, more significantly, the supporting Annex set out the basic philosophy that underpins much of the recommendations of the Code in respect of the level of protection that should be adopted; they define the fire protection objectives and the factors to consider in determining how they may best be achieved. When we come to consider the 'prescriptive' approach, we will find that the 'prescription' is simply a translation of this basic philosophy into a set of recommendations that will fit 'typical' dwelling types.

Secondly, the principles of fire risk assessment provide a basis for the Code to be applied in a flexible and commonsense manner. By explaining where the 'standard' prescriptive recommendations on system Category actually come from (instead of, as sometimes occurs in codes of practice, blandly stating recommendations that can become a source of bemusement to unfortunate users of the Code), it enables intelligent application of the recommendations, and some variation from them where it is appropriate to do so; a simplistic form of 'fire engineering' applied to a very simple type of occupancy!

However, clause 4 also encourages a specifier to tailor-make the design, and in particular the level of protection, for a particular dwelling, where occupant characteristics are known and the dwelling already exists, so making it possible to carry out an inspection. The guidance in Annex A in particular can be used as a basis for determining the appropriate areas to be protected and the types of detection to be used.

In carrying out a fire risk assessment, as advocated in clause 4, the Code suggests that fire detection be regarded as just one component of an engineered approach to fire safety. Accordingly, it is expected that, in this approach, system design should take into account the contribution of all other fire precautions to the reduction of risk.

The Code does not give examples of such fire precautions or how they are to be taken into account. However, these could include the presence of fire resisting doorsets or, say, a domestic sprinkler installation. In this connection, it should be noted that there has been a growth in the use of domestic sprinkler installations in the UK over the past few years, particularly in dwellings in which it is proposed that structural fire precautions will not accord with prescriptive guidance. So, for example, if, in a large property, one wing in which no one sleeps were separated from the sleeping accommodation by fire resisting doors, there might be some justification for omitting to install smoke detectors throughout all the corridor areas of that wing, provided that the means of escape from the sleeping accommodation did not pass through the wing. (This would, of course, depend on the fire risk to occupants in the wing during the day.) Similarly, if a domestic sprinkler system were installed, the extent of the fire detection might be relaxed, although a basic level of escape route protection would still normally be necessary.

The Code recommends that a balance be struck between fire risk and the protection provided, in order that a cost effective solution be achieved. Remember though that, as defined in the Code, fire risk is not simply the probability of fire, but a combination of the probability of fire and the consequences of fire.

Obviously, we want the fire detection system to be reliable and operating correctly at the time of a fire. This is an engineering matter. But there is no such thing as infinite reliability; all systems will develop faults at some time. As we improve the reliability (say, by adding a standby power supply), and reduce the down time (say, by improving the monitoring), we add cost to the system.

The additional cost may not be worthwhile if the fire risk is already low. A single source of power may then be perfectly acceptable in the case of retrofitted smoke alarms. Of course, there will be a finite probability that the power supply will fail. Nevertheless, if the probability of fire is already low, the probability of a power supply failure just at the very time there is a fire might possibly be so low as to be acceptable. Equally, the probability of fire may actually increase at the time of power supply failure, as a result of the more commonplace use of candles in dwellings than was the case even a few years ago. Moreover, if the fire risk is high, the additional cost associated with greater reliability may be warranted.

Similarly, we also want to ensure that fire is detected at an early stage and that the audible warning will be so loud that no one could sleep through it. But to increase the probability of early detection we need more detectors. To increase the probability of rousing people from sleep, we need higher sound levels at their bedheads, which means more sounders or smoke alarms than we might otherwise provide. The additional cost may or may not be justifiable, according to the level of fire risk.

The Code describes this balance between fire risk on the one hand and both system reliability and 'success rate' (in achieving the objective of early detection and warning occupants) on the other hand by means of a diagram (see figure 1).

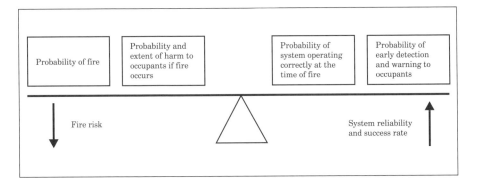

Figure 1 Balance between fire risk and system reliability and success rate

Without such a balance the system will either be unnecessarily expensive or will offer inadequate protection.

If we consider the four components shown in figure 1, the factors that should be considered are fairly obvious. A number of them have already been discussed in this chapter; they are summarized below.

Probability of Fire: Depends on ignition sources, fire prevention measures and, to some extent, the nature and lifestyle of the occupants.
Probability and Extent of Harm (if fire occurs): Depends on means of escape, number of storeys, occupant characteristics, etc.
Probability of Correct System Operation: Depends on system reliability, level of monitoring, level of maintenance, etc.
'Success Rate' of System: Depends on number and location of detectors, sound level of the alarm, hearing and state of occupants, etc.

It is only a simple, qualitative assessment of fire risk, based on experience, that is envisaged in the Code. Fire statistics are simply a mathematical and objective expression of experience, and so Annex A of the Code recommends that it is on these that the fire risk assessment can be based. The recommended approach involves firstly an assessment of the risk on a room-by-room basis.

When any room is considered, the Code recommends that a form of base line be established by identifying from fire statistics the relative likelihood of a fire in a room of that type. A table in the Code provides this information (see figure 2). We can, for example, see from the table that the most common place for fire to start is the kitchen. Because national fire statistics involve very large numbers of incidents, information such as this tends not to change dramatically from one year to another. However, there can be slow trends over a number of years, and this should be borne in mind when using statistical information contained in the Code.

Table I — Relative frequency of fire in rooms within dwellings[4]	
Room	**Proportion of all domestic fires**
Kitchen	54%
Bedroom, bedsitting room	12%
Living room, dining room	12%
Access area	6%
Refuse area	3%
Store room	2%
Bathroom, cloakroom, WC	2%
Roof space	1%
Laundry	1%
Airing cupboard, drying cupboard	1%
Miscellaneous and unknown	7%

Figure 2 Relative likelihood of fire in different rooms
(Reproduced from BS 5839-6.)

Having established the base line, in simple subjective terms only, the relative probability can be modified up or down according to the sources of ignition

---

[4] Based on information provided by the Office of the Deputy Prime Minister.

within the room. For example, if the kitchen were spacious, well laid out, contained no washing machine, dishwasher or sources of ignition other than a cooker, and the occupants never cooked chips, it might be considered that the likelihood of a fire in the kitchen was less than 'average'.

Similarly, in considering the potential for injury or death to occupants due to a fire in the room, the Code recommends that we begin with 'average' figures, but weight these to take account of, for example, occupant characteristics. Because fire risk depends on both the probability and the consequences of fire, both factors need to be taken into account when we consider the implications of the fire risk assessment for system design. Thus, although fires in the kitchen are common, it is much less common for these fires to result in a fatality. The Code advises that, in all new dwellings, heat detectors be installed in kitchens. However, it is also acknowledged that this is not essential in the case of systems retrofitted into most single-family dwellings. On the other hand, it is essential to site a smoke detector in any adjacent circulation space.

The Code goes on to offer numerous similar 'rules of thumb' that can be used in the fire risk assessment, and the implications for system design are also described. The various factors to consider and their implications for system design are summarized below; the factors are grouped in this Guide, in the same way as they are in Annex A of the Code, into those associated with detection and warning objectives, occupant characteristics, lifestyle factors and those associated with the ignition sources.

It is, however, very important to note that the Code advises that the fire risk in any dwelling to which the Code applies is unlikely ever to be so low as to obviate the need for some form of fire detection and alarm system. This somewhat categoric assertion has implications for all landlords (both private sector and local authority) who rent out domestic accommodation. Given this statement in the Code, it must be questioned whether a landlord has provided a safe environment for tenants, fit for purpose, if there is no form of automatic fire detection. Thus, this advice in the Code could have serious implications for civil liability if someone should die or be seriously injured as a result of a fire in rented accommodation that has no automatic fire detection.

Fire Detection and Warning Objectives

Greatest hazard to occupants is smoke in the escape routes.

Implications for System Design

Smoke detectors should be installed throughout the circulation areas that form the escape routes. (In open plan accommodation, where, say, a lounge forms part of the escape route from an upper floor, this means that there should be a smoke detector in the lounge.) However, if the door of the room of fire origin is closed, smoke detectors in the circulation areas are unlikely to operate early enough to save the life of the occupants of the room of fire origin, which is where just over half of all domestic fire fatalities occur.

Statistics show that high risk rooms for fire to start are living/dining rooms (it is in these rooms that 40% of fatal fires start), with bedrooms representing a lower risk.

This can be used to prioritize protection, but individual circumstances may reverse the priorities.

Sleeping occupants are at risk.

Adequate audibility is required in bedrooms.

Ignition Risk Factors

Smokers' materials and matches are the third most common cause of accidental fires in dwellings, and are the most common cause of fatal fires.

Implications for System Design

If occupants smoke, there is greater justification for smoke detectors in living and dining rooms; if they smoke in bed, consider smoke detection in bedrooms.

Space heating is a common cause of fatalities, and often portable appliances are involved.

If portable heaters or solid-fuel fires are used during the night, there may be justification for smoke detectors in relevant rooms, particularly if they are bedrooms.

A high proportion of fatal fires of electrical origin are started by electric blankets.

Use of electric blankets, particularly by high risk groups, such as the elderly, provides greater justification for smoke detection in bedrooms.

Malicious fire raising is a growing problem, and is now the second most common cause of domestic fires, although it accounts for only 10% of fatalities.

If malicious ignition is likely, the level of protection should be high. If malicious ignition by an outsider is likely, ensure that there is early warning of any fire near the entrance door.

Around half of all fires in dwellings result from accidents while cooking. These fires cause 15% of domestic fire deaths.

Heat detectors should be provided in the kitchens of all new dwellings.

Occupant Risk Factors

Implications for System Design

Elderly people are a high risk group, while young children are at greater risk than older children.

A high level of protection is appropriate for homes of the elderly and homes with several elderly people or young children. (This may involve additional detectors.)

Social deprivation is associated with high risk.

Avoidance of the use of battery-operated smoke alarms in these cases.

Multiple occupation results in increased risk. Certain types of HMO, such as bedsits and sheltered housing plus houses over two storeys, appear to constitute a higher risk.

High level of protection is necessary for high risk HMOs, and the system should then be of high reliability.

Impaired mobility results in a longer escape time.

Detection in rooms may be necessary as compensation.

Lifestyle Risk Factors	Implications for System Design
The number of fires each year started by candles, and the resulting number of injuries, is steadily increasing, as a result of a trend in the use of decorative and scented candles.	Detection in a particular room might be appropriate if there is frequent use of candles in that room, particularly if lit candles could be left unattended near combustibles.
Alcohol consumption and use of drugs are known risk factors.	A high standard of fire detection is warranted if alcohol or substance abuse by occupants occurs on a regular basis. This might comprise fire detectors in the kitchen, lounge and, possibly, certain bedrooms.
Certain medical equipment, such as medical beds and oxygen cylinders, can increase fire risk.	Use of such equipment might justify enhanced fire detection.

All the above considerations relate purely to protection of life, which the Code recommends be an objective of all systems within its scope. Property protection will normally only ever be an additional objective, rather than an alternative objective. If property protection is also an objective, the Code recommends that the automatic detection of fire should result in early summoning of the fire service, normally by automatic means. On the other hand, the Code warns that, if the fire service attendance time is long in comparison with the time taken for significant spread of fire, and perhaps water supplies for fire-fighting are limited, additional fire protection measures would be needed to limit fire development until the fire service arrives.

Problems of the above nature sometimes occur in the case of country mansions. Attendance times by fire crews, often retained rather than full time, can be 20 minutes, or more, during which time there can be substantial fire development due to the common absence of fire resisting barriers to compartment the property. On arrival, it may take the fire service a similar length of time to begin to draw water in substantial quantities for main jets.

The nature of the additional fire protection measures required are, of course, outside the scope of the Code. However, clearly they would normally involve some form of compartmentation, but could also include sprinkler protection. Even further outside the scope of the Code is the matter of water supplies, but they should not be overlooked by those responsible for overseeing the entire fire safety package,

The Code describes very briefly an approach to property fire risk assessment. Since property protection is likely to necessitate detection in the area of fire origin, the Code recommends the installation of detectors in at least some rooms. In carrying out a property fire risk assessment, it is recommended that consideration be given to the probability of fire and the probability of discovery before significant spread occurs. The Code suggests that the table showing relative frequency of fire (see figure 2) could be used to prioritize the areas to be protected, while the latter consideration may necessitate the installation of detectors in infrequently visited areas, such as boiler rooms, cellars and roof spaces.

Before leaving the subject of fire risk assessment it might be interesting to re-examine the apparently bold assertion in the Code that, in effect, no home is of low enough risk to be without fire detection. Can the assertion be justified, bearing in mind that around 20% of the population are unconvinced of this?

Personally, I was rather glad to see it. One morning, I announced to my long suffering family that I did not believe the children should be permitted to 'sleep over' with friends who had no smoke alarms in their home, particularly if their parents smoked. Amid moans and groans about Dad being over protective and getting risk out of proportion (put less politely than this), I sat down and performed the following calculation.

Before smoke alarms were widely used, there were around 700 fatal fires each year in single-family dwelling houses. Assuming that there were at the time around 12 million homes, the annual risk of a fatal fire in a home was around one in 17,000. We could assume that the risk today in a home that has no smoke alarms is about the same.

Risks of one in 100,000 per year or less are often regarded as acceptable. (For example, see BS 6651[5] which quantifies various risks associated with everyday life.) A risk of one in 17,000 is higher than the risks for an individual to work in industry for one year or of drowning, which are well recognized and deserve attention. I think this probably justifies the advice given in the Code.

Of course, if one only spends a single night in an unprotected home, the risk of a fatal fire diminishes to around one in 6 million. On the face of it this may be acceptable, and it could be argued that, while the risk to the normal occupants of an unprotected dwelling is unacceptable, the risk to the occasional visitor is acceptable. However, the risk of death I have calculated above is no less than that involved in travelling about ten miles

---

[5] BS 6651: 1999. *Code of practice for protection of structures against lightning.*

by road, where we all take simple precautions like expecting children to wear seat belts. Expecting them to have the protection of smoke alarms, I contend, is no different. Looked at another way, the probability of one in 6 million is of the same order as the probability of winning the National Lottery in any week, if one purchases just one line. Yet, this is a probability that people consider worthy of their £1 expenditure! Anyway, I think the family were convinced. Sadly, the very next day, television brought the news of the deaths of seven children in a fire. One of them was a friend of the other children, sleeping over with the family in a house without working smoke alarms.

System engineering

While Annex A of the Code describes a first principles approach to tailor-making the level of protection by means of fire risk assessment, Annex B ('Choice of appropriate Grade of fire detection and fire alarm system') describes the pros and cons of the different Grades of system.

Battery-operated smoke alarms and heat alarms are described as affording protection at very low cost, and the Code refers to their ease of installation. However, because of the possibility of battery removal, the Code states that the ability of these devices to detect a fire some years after initial installation is not considered to be high, even though the Code acknowledges the benefits of 'tamper proof' battery access (requiring the use of a special tool) and the availability of long life batteries. The Code also advises that the socio-economic groups at greatest risk from fire are those least able to ensure that batteries are always replaced when necessary.

The Code acknowledges that mains-operated smoke and heat alarms are more reliable than battery-operated devices. However, the Code also highlights a major disadvantage of mains-operated smoke and heat alarms, namely the absence of protection when the electricity supply is interrupted. Examples of the potential causes of interruption are given. These can, of course, be a fault in the actual detector circuit as well as a complete loss of supply to the dwelling.

In virtually all circumstances in which mains-operated smoke alarms are appropriate, the Code recommends that the mains-operated smoke alarms should be provided with a standby supply. A significant change in the 2004 Code is that, for all new dwellings, the Code now recommends that mains-operated smoke alarms should have a standby supply. This is also recommended for existing dwellings in which people might not be able to replace batteries in battery-operated detectors soon after a low battery warning is given.

Mains-operated smoke alarms with a standby supply have rapidly gained popularity over simple mains-operated devices. Many local authorities favour the use of smoke alarms with standby supplies. Note that the Code very carefully refers to standby supplies, as opposed to standby batteries, because one form of standby supply is a capacitor, or bank of capacitors. The use of capacitors instead of batteries as a standby supply is recognized by the Code, and this is considered further in the chapter on power supplies. Capacitors do not, of course, need periodic replacement.

The Code advises that more effective control and monitoring of fire detection systems can be achieved by providing some form of control equipment that supplies power to the detectors from a main and standby supply (i.e. Grades A, B or C systems). The highest standard of control and monitoring is, of course, offered by systems of the type to which BS 5839-1 applies. The Code advises that the additional cost and complexity of such systems can be justifiable where the risk is particularly high. Nevertheless, it is accepted that compliance with all the recommendations of BS 5839-1 may not be necessary; as we have seen, in the case of Grade B systems, the control and indicating equipment need not conform to BS EN 54-2. Even simpler control equipment may be used in the case of a Grade C system, in which, for example, as discussed in chapter 5, the detectors might be incorporated with an intruder alarm system.

9. System selection: The prescriptive approach

As discussed in the previous chapter, clause 4 of the Code recommends that final system design should, where practicable, be based on a fire risk assessment. This is all very well in theory but, in practice, when dealing with a specification for a new and as yet unbuilt dwelling, it is not possible. This is accepted in the Code. Moreover, in practice, an electrician required by a householder to install some smoke alarms, with no greater guidance than that, is unlikely to be concerned too much with digesting the mini-treatise in Annex A of the Code on fire risk assessment and fire safety philosophies. There are, indeed, probably many other users of the Code who will basically wish simply to be told exactly what to install, without having to worry too much about the reasons why.

Happily, the Code caters for this in clause 9 (Choice of system). The real meat of clause 9 is presented in a table, Table 1 of BS 5839-6 (see figure 3), in which dwellings are divided into a number of broad classes, mainly according to the occupancy (single family, multiple occupation, sheltered housing and housing providing NHS supported living in the community), number of storeys above ground (which has an obvious bearing on fire risk) and size (not greater than 200 m^2, or greater than 200 m^2, on any floor). Other factors that are taken into account in the table include whether the dwelling is new or existing and whether, in the case of existing dwellings, the recommendations of BS 5588-1[6] (or the guidance that supports national building regulations) are satisfied.

In Table 1 of BS 5389-6 (figure 3), we find the minimum Grades and Categories of system recommended for a typical dwelling in each of the broad classes. Thus, the reader could, almost, ignore clause 4, Annex A

---

[6] BS 5588-1: 1990. *Fire precautions in the design, construction and use of buildings – Code of practice for residential buildings.*

and Annex B, going instead straight to clause 9 for definitive guidance. However, clause 4 and the two relevant Annexes provide the basis on which table 1 was formulated. They should certainly be considered, especially in the case of an existing dwelling, particularly if the fire risk is not quite 'typical' of that normally encountered in the specific class of dwelling. This enables the user of the Code to depart from the generic recommendations of the table if it is appropriate to do so.

Of course there must, to some extent, be a certain arbitrary nature to some of the limitations in table 1. Obviously, someone living in a house of 201 m² on each floor is not at any greater risk than someone living in a house of 199 m² per floor. Nevertheless, there must be some form of 'cut off', above which houses should be protected to a higher standard than 'small houses', possibly even by some form of composite fire alarm system rather than smoke alarms. Hopefully, common sense will prevail in borderline cases and enforcing authorities will exercise some flexibility.

At first sight, table 1 of the Code appears very complex. However, this is merely because it caters for a wide and comprehensive variety of dwelling types. When the table is actually applied to any particular dwelling, it is reasonably clear and straightforward to use, giving a definitive prescription for the appropriate system. However, some insight into the recommendations incorporated in the table, and some elaboration, may be helpful to the reader. This is given in the paragraphs below.

BS 5588-1

BS 5588-1 is a code of practice that advises on fire precautions in the design, construction and use of houses, flats, maisonettes and sheltered housing. It is intended to address only new dwellings, alterations to existing dwellings and conversions of non-residential buildings to form dwellings. The standards recommended for means of escape, etc. are generally equivalent to those required under building regulations. A dwelling constructed in accordance with building regulations/BS 5588-1 should have satisfactory means of escape and compartmentation. Many existing dwellings meet the same standards as those currently applicable to new dwellings. However, in some cases these modern standards may not be satisfied, in which case it should be endeavoured, in the design of the fire detection and alarm system, to compensate, at least to some extent (albeit it may not be possible to fully compensate), for deficiencies.

In traditional single- or two-storey houses, there are usually few requirements in respect of means of escape. The main recommendation of BS 5588-1 is that a habitable room (i.e. any room other than a kitchen, utility room, bathroom, dressing room or w.c.) should not be an inner room unless it is provided with a door or window that is suitably designed for escape or rescue. (An inner room is one from which escape is possible only by passing through another 'access' room.) Inner rooms should not be found at all at floor levels higher than 4.5 m above ground (as could otherwise occur in houses of three or more storeys). Guidance that supports national building regulations also include recommendations for windows on the first floor of a multi-storey house, by which occupants could escape, or be rescued, in the event of fire.

Imagine, now, that a contractor is installing smoke alarms in a house in which there is a bedroom directly off a lounge, but there is no suitable window for escape. It would be prudent to install a detector in the lounge to give early warning to the occupants of the bedroom before they are trapped by a fire in the lounge. (This would also be prudent even if a window were available, albeit that the arrangement would comply with building regulations.) Thus, where the structural fire precautions do not comply with BS 5588-1 (or guidance that supports building regulations), the Code recommends compensating detection, so creating an LD2 system, instead of the minimum standard of LD3 otherwise recommended for retrofitting in most existing dwellings.

Fire alarm contractors and electricians cannot, of course, be expected to be conversant with BS 5588-1 or building regulations. The above simple example relates to a fairly obvious risk. However, what if there is a window in the bedroom? How is the contractor to know the design parameters of a window suitable for escape or rescue? Also, what about three and four-storey houses, where additional fire precautions, such as protected staircases, are recommended by BS 5588-1? How is an electrical contractor expected to recognize all deviations from BS 5588-1?

In practice, a contractor cannot possibly be expected to possess this level of expertise. However, this does not make the distinction drawn in the Code between dwellings that comply with BS 5588-1 and those that do not either valueless or wrong. Nevertheless, this guidance is, possibly, more appropriate for the architect or fire safety professional to consider than, say, an electrical contractor.

Table I — Minimum Grade and Category of fire detection and fire alarm system for protection of life in typical dwellings

Class of dwelling	Minimum Grade and Category of system for installation in:					
	New or materially altered dwellings complying with the recommendations of BS 5588-1 or guidance that supports national building regulations[a]		Existing dwellings complying with the recommendations of BS 5588-1 or guidance that supports national building regulations[a]		Existing dwellings where structural fire precautions are of a lower standard than those recommended in BS 5588-1 or guidance that supports national building regulations[a]	
	Grade	Category	Grade	Category	Grade	Category
Single-family dwellings[b] and shared houses[c] with no floor greater than 200 m² in area						
Owner-occupied bungalow, flat or other single-storey unit	D	LD2[d]	F[e]	LD3[f]	D	LD2[g]
Rented bungalow, flat or other single-storey unit	D	LD2[d]	F[e) h]	LD3[f]	D	LD2[g]
Owner-occupied maisonette or owner-occupied two-storey house	D	LD2[d]	F[e]	LD3[f]	D	LD2[g]
Rented maisonette or rented two-storey house	D	LD2[d]	D	LD3[f]	D	LD2[g]
Three-storey house	D	LD2[d]	D	LD3[f]	D	LD2[g]
Four- (or more) storey house	B	LD2[d]	D	LD2[d) i]	B	LD2[d) g]

Single-family dwellings[b] and shared houses[c] with one or more floors greater than 200 m² in area						
Bungalow, flat or other single-storey unit	D	LD2[d]	D	LD3[f]	D	LD2[g]
Maisonette or two-storey house	B	LD2[d]	B	LD2[d] i)	B	LD2[d] g)
Three- (or more) storey house	Grade A, Category LD2, with detectors sited in accordance with the recommendations of BS 5839-1 for a Category L2[d] i) j) system					

a) In England and Wales, Approved Document B published by the Office of the Deputy Prime Minster. In Scotland, the Technical Standards published by the Scottish Executive. In Northern Ireland, Technical Booklet E published by the Department of Finance and Personnel.

b) Including dwellings with long-term lodgers, but not boarding houses, the latter of which are outside the scope of this part of BS 5839.

c) Houses shared by no more than six persons, generally living in a similar manner to a single family (e.g. houses rented by a number of students).

d) Heat detectors should be installed in every kitchen and the principal habitable room (see 3.28). Where more than one room might be used as the principal habitable room, a heat detector should be installed in each of these rooms.

e) Grade E if there is any doubt regarding the ability of the occupier to replace batteries in battery-operated smoke alarms soon after a battery warning is given (see 9.1.1) but Grade D, if, in addition, there is a significant likelihood of the electricity supply being disconnected because the occupier is unable to pay for supplies.

f) Category LD2 if a risk assessment justifies the provision of additional detectors (see Clause 4).

g) Detectors should be of a type and be so located as to compensate for the lower standard of structural fire precautions (for example, a smoke detector should be installed in the access room to a habitable inner room that has no door or window through which escape is possible). Further detectors might be necessary if a risk assessment justifies their provision. In some cases, a Category LD1 system might be necessary.

h) The batteries in the smoke alarm(s) should have an anticipated life (taking into account monthly testing and fire alarm signals with an aggregate duration of 100 minutes per annum) of at least five years. Removal of batteries should necessitate the use of a tool.

i) Further detectors might be necessary if a risk assessment justifies their provision.

j) BS 5839-1 recommends that detectors are installed in escape routes and, generally, in rooms opening onto escape routes. Notwithstanding the recommendations of BS 5839-1, detectors may be omitted from rooms opening directly onto staircase landings and opening onto escape corridors of six metres or less in length.

Figure 3 Minimum Grade and Category of fire detection and fire alarm system for protection of life in typical dwellings

Table 1 — Minimum Grade and Category of fire detection and fire alarm system for protection of life in typical dwellings (cont.)

Class of dwelling	Minimum Grade and Category of system for installation in:					
	New or materially altered dwellings complying with the recommendations of BS 5588-1 or guidance that supports national building regulations[a]		Existing dwellings complying with the recommendations of BS 5588-1 or guidance that supports national building regulations[a]		Existing dwellings where structural fire precautions are of a lower standard than those recommended in BS 5588-1 or guidance that supports national building regulations[a]	
	Grade	Category	Grade	Category	Grade	Category
Houses in multiple occupation[k] (HMOs)						
HMOs of one or two storeys with no floor greater than 200 m² in area	D	LD2[d]	D	LD3[f) f)]	D	LD2[j) g)]
Other HMOs:						
Individual dwelling units, within the HMO, comprising two or more rooms	D[m]	LD2[d]	D[m]	LD3[n]	D[m]	LD2[g]
Communal areas of the HMO	Grade A, Category LD2, with detectors sited in accordance with the recommendations of BS 5839-1 for a Category L2 system[o]					
Sheltered housing (individual dwelling units only)[p]	C	LD2[d]	C[q]	LD3[f]	C[q]	LD2[g]

Housing providing NHS supported living in the community						
Dwellings of one, two or three storeys occupied by no more than six residents	C	LDI	C	LDI	C	LDI
Other dwellings	Grade A, Category LD1, with detectors sited in accordance with the recommendations of BS 5839-1 for a Category L1 system					

k) Other than houses with long-term lodgers and houses shared by no more than six persons, generally living in a similar manner to a single family (e.g. houses rented by a number of students).

l) Detectors should be installed in communal circulation routes and within any circulation spaces in individual dwelling units comprising two or more rooms (e.g. in hallways and on staircase landings).

m) The detectors in individual dwelling units may be incorporated within the system installed in communal areas.

n) Category LD2 if a risk assessment justifies the provision of additional detectors (see Clause **4**). For example, the conditions in a single-room bedsit might be such that the provision of a heat or smoke detector in the bedsit is justifiable.

o) Heat detectors should be installed in every communal kitchen. Heat or smoke detectors, as appropriate (taking into account the fire risk and the potential for false alarms), should be installed in every communal lounge.

p) See also **20.2q**).

q) Many social alarm systems installed in sheltered housing have facilities for connection, monitoring and separate identification of signals from smoke alarms. If an existing social alarm system does not provide such a facility, it might be acceptable to install a Grade D system, provided that any fire signal is relayed to the warden's accommodation (see recommendation **20.2q**)).

Figure 3 (cont.) Minimum Grade and Category of fire detection and fire alarm system for protection of life in typical dwellings

Distinctions between new and existing buildings

It may be questioned as to why the Code makes a clear distinction between new dwellings and existing dwellings in cases where both comply with BS 5588-1. In some cases, the recommendations are significantly different in each case. For example, for normal-sized, existing owner-occupied single- or two-storey houses, and rented bungalows or flats, battery-operated smoke alarms in the circulation areas are considered to be sufficient. However, for new dwellings of the above type, the Code recommends mains-operated smoke alarms, with a standby supply, in the circulation areas, plus equivalently powered heat alarms in the kitchen and principal habitable room (i.e. the lounge).

The answer is simply that it was considered that the low cost and ease of retrofitting battery-operated smoke alarms in existing dwellings probably outweigh the disadvantages of these devices in cases where the fire risk is not unduly high. In the case of a single-storey dwelling, means of escape may be easier in the event of fire than for those sleeping upstairs in a two-storey house when fire occurs in, say, the living room, which is the most common room for a fatal fire to occur at night. As discussed below, owner occupiers are less at risk from fire than those in rented accommodation. Accordingly, the Code does not distinguish between the risk to occupants in two-storey owner-occupied houses and that in single-storey owner-occupied houses.

The continued acceptance of battery-operated smoke alarms for retrofitting in owner-occupied houses also reflects custom and practice on the part of householders. There is little point in recommending that householders retrofit only mains-operated devices when it is known that, in practice, householders will not do so because of the cost, need for the use of a qualified electrician and possible effects on the décor; in practice, householders will continue to nip down to the local D-I-Y outlet and buy battery-operated smoke alarms that they can fit themselves.

On the other hand, when a new dwelling is being built, it is much easier to install mains-operated devices, and the cost difference in installing mains-operated devices with a standby supply, as opposed to mains-only devices, is negligible. Given that fatal fires have been known to occur at times of power failure, and that the increasing availability of candles in many dwellings is likely to increase the fire risk at such times, the enhancement in safety at little cost, by the use of devices with a standby supply, is very easy to justify.

More philosophically, it is a recognized principle in fire safety that standards for new premises (of any type) are not usually applied retrospectively to existing premises. This is more a matter of practicality. It is not practicable to upgrade or replace fire precautions every time a new standard is published. On the other hand, it cannot ever be claimed that standards applied to new premises should not exceed those found in existing premises. If that were so, standards could never be improved.

It could, of course, be argued that the second column of table 1 is not intended to apply to dwellings that already have smoke alarms, but only to the installation of new smoke alarms in an existing dwelling; since the 'system' is new, why should the standards for a new system in a new dwelling not be applied? While there is some merit in this argument, from the point of view of the householder it would seem illogical that the householder should be told not to retrofit a battery-operated smoke alarm when the householder's neighbours are still protected by the battery-operated smoke alarms they purchased and installed in the past. Moreover, the 19% or so of householders yet to install smoke alarms are clearly reluctant to do so. It is better that they be persuaded to install low cost, easily installed battery-operated smoke alarms than be given the implication that only the installation of mains-operated devices is worthwhile; if they have still not installed battery-operated devices, they are unlikely to be willing to go to the trouble of installing mains-operated devices.

Note also that the Code recommends that mains-operated smoke alarms be used if there is any doubt that the occupier will be able to replace batteries in Grade F systems soon (the Code suggests typically no more than five days) after a low battery warning indication. Why five days? At first sight, the five days cannot relate directly to battery capacity at the time the fault warning is first given, since a low battery warning will, in the absence of a fire, continue for at least 30 days.

However, the householder could become frustrated with the periodic audible warning and remove the battery as soon as it sounds. The worst case would occur if this were done as soon as it began to sound. The householder could then be left without protection for five days. What is the chance of a fatal fire in the dwelling during this time? In the previous chapter it was suggested that, in the absence of fire detection, the probability of a fatal fire in one household during any year would be in the region of 1 in 17,000. The chance of the fatal fire occurring in a five day period is then around 1 in a million. If the battery can be replaced within five days, this would suggest a person who can, or does, go shopping more than once a week. Even if they forget the battery on the first occasion, the chance of a fatal fire when the dwelling is unprotected is still at least a million to one but, in practice, the 'odds' are probably higher because they shop twice a week.

Now consider the person who goes shopping once a week but forgets to buy a battery on their next shopping visit. They could be left without protection for 14 days; the risk of a fatal fire increases to about half a million to one; this is still a very low 'average' risk, but bearing in mind that, for those with particular risk factors, it becomes greater, the advice in the Code ensures that the use of battery-operated smoke alarms does not result in undue risk due to low batteries.

Distinction between owner-occupier and rented dwellings

Although not always discussed in the politically correct environment of today, as discussed in the Code there is an established correlation between the incidence of fire and various social indicators. As long ago as 1979, one study[7] showed a distinct correlation between the rate of fires in London boroughs and the percentage of non-owner occupation in the boroughs. Many subsequent surveys, such as the British Crime Survey, as well as common experience, verify the correlation between social deprivation and fire risk. Socially deprived people are unlikely to be home owners.

In the case of two-storey houses, the restriction in the use of battery-operated smoke alarms to owner-occupied dwellings is consistent with the implications in Annex B of the Code that, for those at greatest risk, including socially deprived people, who are unlikely to be owner occupiers, more reliable power sources should be used. Even in the case of single-storey properties, a distinction is made between rented and owner-occupied properties. In the former case, reliability of operation on demand is increased by the recommendation that only 'tamper proof' long life batteries should be used.

Relevance of number of floors above ground level

In BS 5588-1 and guidance that supports building regulations, the standards recommended for means of escape become more onerous as the dwelling increases in height, due to the greater difficulty in both escape and rescue as the height increases. The original version of BS 5588-1 referred to one, two-, three- and four-storey houses, but the heights are now expressed in terms of number of floors more than 4.5 m above ground level, presumably because the risk associated with a three-storey house with very high ceilings could be the same as that in a four-storey house with lower ceilings; in both

---

[7] *The incidence of residential fires in London – the effect of housing and other social factors.* BRE Information Paper 20/79 S. E. Chandler.

cases, those on the top floor might be the same height above ground level. The 1995 version of BS 5839-6 adopted the same approach in specifying height above ground level. However, for simplification, particularly in the case of retrofitting by small electrical contractors, the 2004 version of the Code uses number of storeys above ground as the relevant pointer, rather than the height above ground.

BS 5839-6 reflects the greater risk associated with greater height by recommending a higher standard of system engineering and, in some cases additional fire detection.

Reference to L2 standard in BS 5839-1

For large houses of three or more storeys and most HMOs, BS 5839-6 recommends a Grade A system, but advises that the siting of detectors should be in accordance with the recommendations of BS 5839-1 for a Category L2 system. This means that detectors should be provided in escape routes, rooms adjoining escape routes and in a number of other areas.

The Code qualifies the reference to L2 in two respects. Firstly, in short corridors it permits a relaxation from the provision of detectors in rooms adjoining escape routes. The purpose of these detectors is to give a warning before the door to the room fails and smoke enters the escape route in substantial quantities. The need for these detectors was identified in research carried out for the Home Office by the Fire Research Station. In this research, it was established that, in relatively long corridors, such as can be found in hotels, smoke from a room may, in some circumstances, smoke log the corridor before operating detectors spaced at the normal distances within the corridor. This can occur if relatively cool, tarry smoke drops in height before travelling far enough laterally to reach the detector.

If the corridor is quite short, the risk to occupants is less. The distance they must traverse is correspondingly short, and, in a dwelling, they are likely to be familiar enough with the escape route to make a dash through a short length of corridor. More importantly, in a short corridor, the door of any room is not very far from the nearest detector, and the problem described above is not likely to occur. Accordingly, the Code relaxes the particular recommendation in the case of corridors less than 6 m in length. If the detector is located halfway along the corridor, the maximum distance between the door of any adjoining room and the detector should be less than 3 m. (This figure of 6 m overrides the figure of 4 m used in the equivalent relaxation in BS 5839-1.)

Anyone specifying Category L2 protection should define the areas in which detectors are to be installed over and above the areas that are required to be protected in a Category L3 system. The Code does this by advising that, in the case of an HMO, in addition to the escape routes, detectors should be installed in any communal kitchen and in any communal lounge. However, where detection is retrofitted in an existing HMO, it is not specifically recommended that detectors be installed within kitchens and lounges in each self-contained unit of accommodation. In existing single-family houses of four or more storeys, and large dwellings of two or more storeys, the equivalent recommendation is that heat detectors should be retrofitted in every kitchen and the principal habitable room.

Property protection

The guidance in table 1 applies only to protection of life. Property protection is addressed in table 2, which is much simpler in nature (see figure 4).

The systems within the scope of the Code are recommended only for protection of single- and two-storey dwellings. For larger properties, a BS 5839-1 Category P1 system is recommended. However, some of the guidance in Part 6 on, for example, detector types, avoidance of false alarms, and manual call points could still be regarded as useful supplementary advice. It is, of course, likely that the P1 system will actually be intended, in practice, to protect life, in which case the life safety recommendations of Part 6 may be adopted in conjunction with the property protection recommendations of Part 1. This simultaneous use of both Codes is briefly mentioned in Part 6, and it would be possible to have a BS 5839-1 Category P1 system combined with a BS 5839-6 Grade A Category LD3 system!

Table 2 — Minimum Grade and Category of fire detection and fire alarm system for protection of property in typical dwellings		
Class of dwelling	**Grade**	**Category**
Single-storey and two-storey dwellings	C	PD2
Other dwellings	A system conforming to the recommendations of BS 5839-1 for a Category P1 system[a]	

[a] May be reduced to P2 if the risk to property from fire, and the maximum potential loss, do not warrant a Category P1 system.

Figure 4 Recommendations of BS 5839-6 for minimum Grades and Categories of system (property protection)

10. Mixed systems

A 'Mixed System' is defined in BS 5839-6 as an arrangement whereby two different Grades of fire detection and fire alarm system are provided within one dwelling for the purpose of satisfying two different fire safety objectives. The concept of 'mixed' systems is addressed in sub-clause 9.1.5 of the Code. When the concept was introduced for the first time when the 1995 version of BS 5839-6 was published, to many people it seemed a strange concept that might not even accord with best practice. Because the idea of such 'mixed' systems is contrary to commonly recognized practices, but the use of these is important in HMOs, a complete chapter has been allocated to the subject in this Guide.

We should firstly note that the Code considers mixed systems to be a special exception to the norm. The advice given is that, normally, even in the largest of dwellings, a single fire detection and alarm system should serve the entire dwelling. When are exceptions to this 'rule' appropriate?

The Code suggests that this may sometimes occur when there are multiple objectives to be satisfied. Under these circumstances, it may be appropriate to use different forms of fire detection system to satisfy these objectives.

The main reason for introducing this concept in the 1995 version of BS 5839-6 was to give recognition to a special arrangement of mixed systems in HMOs. In actual fact, this arrangement is described in table 1 of the Code, which was considered in the previous chapter (see figure 3).

Before describing the mixed systems in question, and examining the thinking behind their use, it may be useful to consider traditional thinking on fire detection in HMOs. Original guidance on this took the form of a Home Office publication on fire safety in HMOs, often referred to as the 'dark blue guide'. Although, at the time this guide was published, the installation of fire detection in an HMO could only be a recommendation of the local authority (since the relevant legislation in England and Wales required only adequate means of escape until amended in 1989), the guide recommended against the use of smoke alarms in HMOs. Instead a system complying with BS 5839-1 was recommended for houses that were divided into self-contained units and were more than two floors in height (and for hostels of more than one floor). It was generally frowned upon to mix smoke alarms with the BS 5839-1 system.

In 1992, new guidance on fire precautions in HMOs was produced by the then Department of the Environment, in the form of Circular 12/92. This guidance, which remains current, recommends that HMOs that are sub-divided into self-contained units and that are more than two storeys in height (and all parts of hostels) be protected by a BS 5839-1 Category L2 system. However, for single- and two-storey houses, the guidance recommends that consideration be given to the use of smoke alarms. The guide also advises that fire sensors which rely solely on battery power should not be used for premises that are more than two floors in height, implying that they might be suitable for those of two floors or less in height. Note, however, that this guidance does not appear to consider the use of smoke alarms in conjunction with a BS 5839-1 system.

If we consider table 1 of BS 5839-6 (see figure 3), we note that mains-operated smoke alarms with a standby supply are considered acceptable for a single- or two-storey HMO, with the proviso that no floor is greater than 200 m^2 in area. This, in effect, permits HMOs of the size of a normal single-family dwelling house to be protected in the same way as a new single-family dwelling house. In the case of an existing HMO, the smoke alarms should be installed in both the communal circulation areas and circulation areas within any individual dwellings comprising two or more rooms.

For other HMOs, table 1 considers separately the protection of communal areas and the protection of dwelling units comprising two or more rooms. This is because, in each case, the objective is different; we therefore have the situation to which sub-clause 9.1.5 refers.

The protection in the communal areas is to address the risk associated with multiple occupation. In an HMO, the safety of all occupants may be threatened by the behaviour of the most careless occupant. Looked at another way, a fire in any one dwelling unit can grow and eventually threaten the communal escape routes before anyone, other than those in the unit of fire origin, is aware of it. The communal area fire detection is intended to provide a warning to the other occupants before their escape routes become impassable.

This is identical to the function of a BS 5839-1 Category L3 system, in which detectors are installed in circulation areas and rooms adjoining escape routes. The purpose of the latter detectors is not to give early warning to people in the room of fire origin, but to give early warning to everyone else of an impending threat to the communal escape routes. If, in the HMO, there are communal lounges or kitchens, these are high risk areas, in which detection is also necessary.

The high risks associated with HMOs, together with the criticality of early warning of a fire that threatens escape routes, necessitate a highly reliable form of detection; thus, the Code recommends a Grade A system for detection of a fire that threatens escape routes or occurs in these high risk areas. The detectors should be sited in the same way as those in a BS 5839-1 Category L2 system. In practice, this means that there should be optical smoke detectors (not ionization smoke detectors) within all circulation spaces (although it might be possible, in some circumstances, to consider the use of a combination of optical smoke detectors and carbon monoxide detectors), plus detectors in all rooms opening into circulation spaces.

The detectors within rooms opening onto escape routes can be heat, smoke or carbon monoxide fire detectors (subject to limitations in BS 5839-6 on the use of carbon monoxide fire detectors). It should be noted that, in BS 5839-1, to which BS 5839-6 refers for recommendations on siting detectors in the Grade A system used to protect the communal areas, there is an important relaxation in the recommendation for installation of detectors in rooms opening onto escape routes. This relates to short corridors, of no greater than 4 m in length, that are separated from other parts of the escape routes by construction, including any door, that is fire resisting. BS 5839-1 advises that, to protect such short, enclosed corridors, there is no need to install detectors in rooms opening onto them.

When this relaxation was drafted for inclusion in BS 5839-1, it was for certain HMOs that it was regarded as particularly relevant. In some large houses that are divided into bedsits, some of these bedsits often open directly onto a staircase, while sometimes, on a landing of the staircase there is a door leading into a very short corridor or small lobby, off which there may be, say, just two rooms. Before BS 5839-1: 2002 was published, compliance with the 1988 version of that Code would have necessitated a smoke detector in the corridor and a detector of some sort in both rooms. Under the 2002 version of BS 5839-1, the detectors in the rooms can be omitted if the corridor or lobby is no more than 4 m in length.

Having satisfied the objective of warning people in an HMO when there is a fire in a unit other than their own, there is still a need to satisfy a completely different objective, namely to give people early warning of a fire in their own unit of accommodation (just as in the case of a purpose-built flat, maisonette or any other single-family dwelling). The Code accepts that, for an existing HMO, this may be achieved by installing mains-powered smoke alarms with a standby supply within the circulation spaces of each individual dwelling unit, just as one would in a new flat.

Thus, a large existing HMO could, for example, be protected in accordance with the Code in the manner described below.

- A Grade A system with:
  - smoke detectors in the communal corridors,
  - heat or smoke detectors in any communal lounges, plus heat detectors in any communal kitchens,
  - a heat detector just inside the door to each flat.
- A Grade D system in each dwelling unit comprising mains-operated smoke alarms with a standby supply in the circulation areas of the unit.

If each dwelling unit comprised just a single room (e.g. a bedsit), the Code permits the specifier to dispense with the smoke alarms entirely, because there is now no internal circulation area; using the analogy of an existing typical single-family dwelling house, the minimum level of protection does not necessitate detectors within individual rooms. (Even in new single-family dwellings, and in each flat in a new HMO, the Code recommends heat alarms in the kitchen and principal habitable room, but not specifically in bedrooms.)

Note that by specifying Grade D as the minimum system Grade for protecting the individual dwellings, the Code does not preclude the use of a single fire alarm system throughout the property, with smoke detectors in the circulation areas of each unit, connected to the single, Grade A system; this would then obviate the need for the heat detectors just inside the doors. The smoke detectors in the units of accommodation would seem to satisfy both the relevant objectives; if fire occurred in a unit of accommodation, they would warn people beyond the unit of accommodation and people in the unit of accommodation. Indeed, the use of a single system might simplify maintenance. In this connection, the Code recommends that, if the mixed system option is used, it is important to make occupiers aware of the need for testing and maintenance of their smoke alarms, over and above any testing and maintenance of the Grade A system in the communal parts.

Why then would one wish to use a mixed system? The reason lies in the age old problem of false alarms. If (or more likely when) the smoke detectors within the dwelling units produce false alarms, it is desirable that other occupiers are not disturbed. Constant false alarms in an HMO can lead to a lowering of fire safety, because occupants begin to ignore fire alarm signals. I have even known one case where the fire alarm control panel was vandalized beyond repair; because of a shortcoming in the replacement panel, two occupants came very close to losing their lives because the system failed to operate correctly when a fire occurred.

The use of smoke alarms in dwellings within an HMO provides, in most cases, acceptably reliable warning to occupants if a fire occurs in their own accommodation, without disturbing anyone else when false alarms occur. If a fire occurs and grows to an extent that constitutes a threat to others, it should be detected by the Grade A system. Thus, we have two separate objectives fulfilled by two different systems.

Since the mixed system concept was introduced in 1995, it has been found by enforcing authorities to work very successfully in HMOs. It enables occupants to 'live' with the fire detection arrangements, as occupants are not constantly disturbed by the false alarms of their neighbours. They will only suffer the same false alarms typically suffered by occupiers of any single-family dwelling. If, as can happen in a single family dwelling, they disconnect their smoke alarm(s), they only endanger themselves, as other occupants would be adequately warned by a heat detector within the Grade A system in the unit of fire origin.

In some existing HMOs, there may be a need for further detectors in certain rooms of each dwelling unit. It has already been noted that, in a new HMO, the Code recommends the installation of heat detectors in the kitchen and principal habitable room. The purpose of these is merely to give an enhanced warning to occupants of the unit of fire origin, and so heat alarms, interlinked with a smoke alarm in the circulation area of the unit, would suffice. On the other hand, there would be no real harm in using heat detectors that form part of the Grade A system, as heat detectors rarely produce false alarms.

However, detectors within rooms of a dwelling unit in an HMO might be required for another purpose. In an HMO, each dwelling unit should be separated from each other dwelling unit by one-hour fire resisting construction. It might, nevertheless, be acceptable to an enforcing authority if, say, existing lath and plaster ceilings (which would not afford a fire resistance of one hour) were permitted to remain, provided heat detectors were installed in every room of each dwelling, other than, possibly, toilets and bathrooms. These detectors would then serve to warn occupants of the unit above the unit of fire origin before the lath and plaster ceiling failed, so permitting fire spread to the unit above. For this purpose, if a mixed system were used in the HMO, these heat detectors would, of course, need to form part of the Grade A system.

A mixed system may sometimes also be found in sheltered housing or certain blocks of flats. In these cases, the Code advises that any detection in communal areas is outside the scope of the Code and that any system protecting communal areas should comply with BS 5839-1. The provision of such a system would not, however, preclude the provision of smoke alarms within the individual dwelling units.

One further example of a mixed system is given in the Code. This relates to the situation in which one system might be used for property protection (e.g. a Grade B Category PD2 system), while for protection of life a Grade D Category LD3 system might be installed throughout circulation areas. This situation is much less likely to occur, but it is theoretically possible. It might, for example, occur if the householder had a small office area within the house, which he or she wished to be protected with a small fire detection system, perhaps with a facility for remote transmission of alarms. For protection of the occupants, there might also be smoke alarms in the circulation areas of the house.

11. Silencing and disablement facilities

The subject of silencing or disablement of a fire detection and alarm system can be highly contentious. There is a view by some in the fire safety field that, in dwellings, there should be no means whereby occupants can readily access facilities that would silence or disable the system. In the case of smoke alarms, it is sometimes claimed that false alarms can even be a good thing, proving that the smoke alarms are operating correctly. If a false alarm does occur, normally it is not too difficult to stop the alarm by simply waving a towel around the offending smoke alarm. The connection of smoke alarms to lighting circuits is often cited as a good means of preventing mains-operated smoke alarms from being disabled by isolation of their mains power supply.

False alarms can, nevertheless, be a barrier to more widespread use of smoke alarms, and the disruption they create can be exacerbated if the alarm cannot be silenced. False alarms are almost certainly one reason that some people do not maintain their smoke alarms in working order. A prolonged false alarm that cannot readily be silenced by use of the tea towel can occur in the event of certain detector faults, contamination of detectors, ingress of insects into the detector chamber, etc. Under these circumstances, occupants may, in frustration, irreparably damage the smoke alarm in order to silence it. Certainly, they will find some means of stopping the noise.

In 1994, the Consumer Product Safety Commission in the USA reported that 20% of homes visited in the National Smoke Detector Project had detectors with dead batteries, or with missing or disconnected power sources. In about a quarter of these cases, the householder had experienced problems with the detectors. The second most common problem reported in these cases was that the detector alarmed continuously when powered. This problem was found in over 1% of the homes involved in the survey. This figure is quite low and, in some cases, the problem may actually have been associated with the low battery chirp. However, if the problem were repeated in the UK, it could well be the case that some 100,000 homes in the UK currently have unpowered detectors that would alarm continuously if powered.

Since it is known that, under certain circumstances, prolonged false alarms can occur, it seems unreasonable to take the view that the householder must simply suffer from the nuisance of false alarms in order to be sufficiently safe. This would be particularly unreasonable now that the installation of smoke detection is no longer a matter of choice but, in new homes, a requirement imposed under legislation. Such an attitude would also ignore the sad fact that people are now dying in dwellings in which smoke alarms have been rendered inoperative, sometimes due to frustration with false alarms. In any case, if the occupant were to replace the smoke alarms with a BS 5839-1 system, the control equipment would, in order to comply with BS EN 54-2, be provided with controls to silence alarms and to disable detectors during, for example, situations that could lead to false alarms.

The 2004 version of the Code places much stronger emphasis than the preceding version on the importance of limiting false alarms and their effects. An important measure in this respect is the provision of facilities to silence false alarms and/or disable the fire detection at times when false alarms are likely. False alarms are the subject of clause 12 of the Code and of chapter 14 of this Guide. However, such is the importance of silencing and disablement facilities that they are the subject of this separate chapter of the Guide.

The intent of the Code is that occupants should have some means whereby, in the event of a prolonged false alarm, the alarm signal can be silenced, if necessary by disablement of at least part of the system. The Code recommends in clause 12.2 that all fire detection and alarm systems within its scope should be provided with accessible means by which the occupier of the dwelling can silence fire alarm signals.

Grade A systems are based on the recommendations of BS 5839-1. Accordingly, BS 5839-6 recommends that Grade A systems have silencing facilities that comply with certain recommendations of BS 5839-1. The effect of this cross-reference to BS 5839-1 is that Grade A systems should have manually operated silencing facilities that, when operated, cause an audible signal to be given at the control and indicating equipment. Use of the control should not affect any visual indicators or prevent alarms from being started or re-started after silencing, nor should it affect any automatic transmission of alarm signals to an alarm receiving centre. If an alarm occurs in a new zone, the alarm sounders should re-sound. Automatic silencing will not normally be appropriate, except in the case of radio-linked sounders, which, unless there is continuous occupation of the property at all times, should silence automatically after 30 minutes.

Similar facilities can be provided in a Grade B system. However, a simpler facility may alternatively be provided in the form of a switch that, effectively, just switches sounders off. They will not then re-start if a further alarm signal occurs; the switch can be a means of disabling the sounder circuit. However, as a reminder to the occupier, an audible warning of at least a half second duration must be given at the control equipment at least once every 10 minutes. If a disablement control of this type is used, it will also prevent false alarms from occurring, but a facility to disable the detectors themselves is also permitted.

In Grade C systems, very simple arrangements to both prevent and silence false alarms are acceptable. There should be a means of silencing both short-term 'unwanted alarms' (see chapter 14), such as those that might occur during cooking, and also permanent alarm signals arising from detector faults, etc. This can, for example, be a switch to disable detectors or one to disable sounders.

In the case of mains-operated smoke alarms (with or without a standby supply), the Code considers silencing of short-term unwanted alarms, such as those resulting from cooking, separately from those resulting from a fault in a detector, etc. In the case of short-term unwanted alarms, two alternatives are offered. The first is an alarm silence facility conforming to the requirements of BS 5446-1, provided it can be operated by occupiers of the dwelling when standing at floor level. (The Code does not state whether, for example, use of a broom handle when standing at floor level would satisfy this recommendation, but this might be a reasonable interpretation, as many occupiers would be unable to reach up to a ceiling-mounted smoke alarm). An alarm silence facility (sometimes called a 'hush button') de-sensitizes, or completely disables, the smoke alarm for a period of up to 15 minutes. If a minimal sensitivity is retained, there is the added advantage that a serious fire will be detected and the alarm raised, but false alarms will not result from activities such as cooking. Thus, the facility can prevent false alarms during cooking, as well as silencing unwanted alarms when they do occur.

The Code does, however, offer an alternative to the provision of an alarm silence facility for silencing short-term alarms. The smoke alarms would be satisfactory without this facility if, instead, all power to the smoke alarm(s) can be isolated by suitable means, without the use of a tool and without isolation of power to other electrical equipment, such as lighting, in the dwelling. This arrangement does not cater well for short-term false alarms even though the Code accepts it, but it does, at least, provide a facility for a non-skilled occupier to power down a smoke alarm that is permanently in alarm.

What would constitute suitable 'means for isolation'? The key factor is that no tool should be involved, not even a simple screwdriver, as, for example, an elderly occupier might not possess any tools, or could be incapable of using them. Nor should any degree of skill be involved. Thus, use of a circuit breaker would be satisfactory for isolation of the mains supply, but removal of a fuse would not. In a Grade D system, removal of the battery without the use of a tool would also need to be possible.

In practice, these recommendations clearly point towards the benefits of an alarm silence facility. This would be necessary if the detectors are supplied from a lighting circuit, unless a further suitable means of isolation is fitted to isolate only the smoke alarms. Moreover, removal of a battery as a means of silencing a short-term unwanted alarm is crude and not particularly desirable.

However, as permanent false alarms as a result of, for example, a faulty smoke alarm would be rare, total power down of a faulty detector is a satisfactory means of dealing with such a problem. The Code accepts this and permits the use of a tool; removal of a fuse is not specifically excluded either. Nevertheless, the means of isolation should not involve isolation of power to other electrical equipment, such as lighting. Accordingly, a facility, such as a fused connection unit, would be necessary if smoke alarms are connected to a lighting circuit.

For Grade F systems, there should also be a means for silencing alarm signals. The Code accepts that this can be by means of battery removal, provided it does not involve the use of a 'special tool', which is defined in the Code as a tool that is not likely to be carried by a member of the general public. Securing the battery by slot headed screws would be acceptable, as many common household objects can serve as a screwdriver in this case. However, again, an alternative is the provision of an alarm silence control. This makes the provision of the control appropriate in many 'tamper proof' battery-operated smoke alarms. The intent is to provide a means for silencing the short-term unwanted alarm, on the assumption that the rare detector fault can, ultimately, be addressed, albeit with additional effort, by battery removal.

In any of the above cases, obviously isolation of the mains supply to a mains-operated smoke alarm is undesirable. However, it is obvious that the BSI committee have endeavoured to avoid, as far as possible, making recommendations that currently available smoke alarms do not satisfy. Many mains-operated smoke alarms have no form of alarm silence control and so the Code accepts other forms of silencing, such as isolation of the circuit and, in the case of Grade D systems, battery removal. However, the recommendation that all systems have some means of silencing, including battery-operated smoke alarms, even though this limits the applications for some current models, is probably some indication of the importance attached to such a facility.

The recommendations for silencing and disablement are, in the form presented above, quite complicated. The reason for this is the number of permutations of alternative arrangements that the Code accepts. To clarify the actual recommendations for any particular situation, figure 5 below represents the author's interpretation of the Code's recommendations.

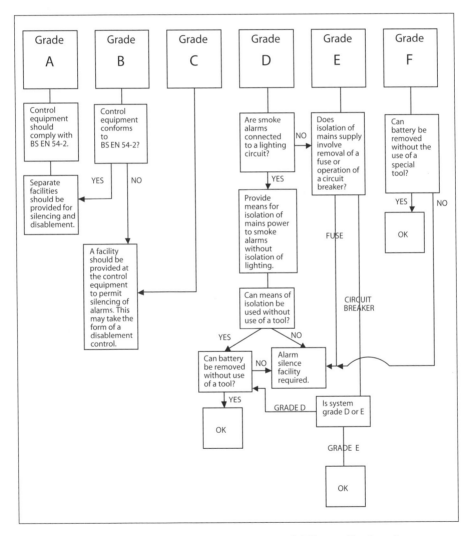

Figure 5 Means for silencing or disablement of different Grades of system

12. Types of fire detector

In terms of detection of fire, there is, in theory, little unique about domestic occupancies that necessitates an approach to detector selection that differs from the considerations applicable to many other occupancies. As in any occupancy, there is a balance between efficiency in detection of fire and avoidance of false alarms; one would not install a smoke detector in a kitchen for example.

Advice on types of fire detector is contained in clause 10 of the Code. Advice on avoidance of false alarms is set out separately in clause 12, because avoidance of false alarms does not just involve selection of the most appropriate type of detector.

In the Commentary of clause 10, the various types of detector – heat, smoke, carbon monoxide and flame – are reviewed rigorously. The Commentary describes the operating principles of, and application for, each type of detector. In practice, of course, the majority of detectors used in dwellings are point-type smoke detectors, and it is in respect of these that the most important advice in clause 10 is given.

The Code is somewhat definitive in its advice on the choice between optical and ionization chamber detectors, and, in this respect, the recommendations accord with those in BS 5839-1. Smoke detected in a circulation area is likely to have travelled from an adjacent room, during which time it is likely to have cooled and the smoke particles are likely to have coalesced; in simple terms, near a flaming fire the smoke consists of a large number of small particles, but as it 'ages' smoke particles 'stick together', so resulting in a smaller number of larger particles.

Since optical detectors are more sensitive to large particles than ionization chamber detectors, the Code recommends that smoke detectors installed in circulation spaces, such as hallways and landings, should be of the optical type. Optical detectors are also recommended for situations in which smouldering plastics are involved (e.g. if a likely cause of fire is ignition of furniture or bedding by a cigarette).

Ionization chamber smoke detectors are suggested as possibly more appropriate than optical detectors if a fast burning fire presents a greater danger than a smouldering fire. Thus, if smoke detectors are installed within rooms, such as the living room or dining room, ionization chamber detectors may be more appropriate.

When we come to consider false alarms (see chapter 12), we shall see that the above advice happily coincides with that associated with false alarm avoidance. However, the advice does mean that smoke detectors in dwellings should predominantly be of the optical type. Even though this recommendation was included in the 1995 version of BS 5839-6, at the time of publication of the 2004 version ionization chamber smoke alarms still predominate because of their lower price. The differential in price, which has been quite substantial due, in part, to the greater popularity of the cheaper ionization chamber smoke alarms as well as true differences in the cost of manufacture, has decreased somewhat in the case of mains-operated smoke alarms.

The 2004 version of the Code acknowledges this custom and practice, but deprecates it in view of the greater potential for ionization chamber smoke detectors to generate false alarms when exposed to fumes from kitchens (see chapter 12), and in view of their poorer response to smouldering fires and to smoke that has drifted some distance from its source. Given that people now die as a result of fires in dwellings in which smoke alarms have been disabled as a result of false alarms, it is to be hoped that all parties, including fire brigades (when they give advice to householders), building control officers (when they enforce building regulations in new dwellings), and those enforcing fire legislation in HMOs, take heed of this recommendation. It is also to be hoped that D-I-Y outlets make optical smoke alarms more readily available; at the time of writing, some only stock ionization chamber smoke alarms.

Other types of smoke detector, including beam type and aspirating type, are briefly discussed in the Code. These are unlikely to find applications in dwellings other than large stately homes, particularly those with high spaces or aesthetically important ceilings on which it may be undesirable to mount point detectors. Similarly flame detectors are unlikely to find any application other than for protection of property in some very large, high spaces.

There is, however, scope for use of heat detectors, particularly since the publication of a standard, BS 5446-2, for domestic heat alarms. The 2004 version of BS 5839-6 gives particular recognition to the role of heat detectors, including heat alarms, for which the standard was first published in 2002. The installation of heat detectors in the kitchen and principal habitable room of all new dwellings is recommended by the Code. This is also recommended in the case of existing houses of four (or more) storeys and in large, two- or more storey dwellings (including maisonettes), if the floor area of any storey exceeds 200 m². Smoke detectors obviously could not be used in a kitchen. They could be installed in the lounge (or any other habitable room), but the Code does not specifically recommend this, as the resultant potential increase in false alarms would be undesirable and a possible barrier to acceptance of the recommendation by householders.

The Code also accepts the use of heat detectors in any room of a dwelling in a Category LD1, LD2 or PD system. There is, however, a proviso, namely that the purpose of installing detection in the room(s) in question is not to protect people who sleep in the rooms nor to protect a high value property and its contents. A heat detector would be unlikely to operate early enough to achieve these objectives. Moreover, the Code notes that a heat detector in the room of fire origin might not give sufficient warning for occupants elsewhere in the dwelling to escape safely if the door to that room is open; equally, in a normal-size house, the nearest smoke detector in the circulation area will operate quite quickly, albeit that there will then possibly be only a short time available for escape. For this reason, it is important that occupiers are still advised to shut all doors at night. Then, the heat detector in the lounge (and kitchen) is, indeed, likely to operate before the smoke detector in the circulation space, warranting the additional provision of these detectors in new and large existing dwellings.

There is now significant lobbying for the greater use of sprinkler systems in dwellings, particularly those of the highest risk, such as certain HMOs, and those occupied by socially deprived people, or people with major mobility impairment, etc. In practice, sprinkler systems are also now sometimes installed in certain dwellings as a 'trade off' for avoidance of specific structural fire precautions, such as complete enclosure of a staircase. The Code accepts that a sprinkler head is a form of heat detector. It is a simple matter to link a sprinkler system to a fire detection and alarm system (by a flow switch). Since a flow switch is simply an on/off device, much in the same way as a manual call point, it would be possible to trigger certain smoke alarm systems this way. In such cases, the Code permits each sprinkler head to be treated as a heat detector for the purpose of compliance with the Code.

In a new dwelling, therefore, sprinkler protection in the kitchen and living room could obviate the need for heat detectors in these rooms. The Code does, however, recommend that the fire detection and alarm system should be activated by the sprinkler system even if mains power to the dwelling has failed. (The pumps of domestic sprinkler systems can be mains operated with no standby supply. Care might be necessary if the flow switch were not triggered by the flow of water as a result of non-operation of the pump.) This limits the application to Grade D systems and above.

Carbon monoxide fire detectors are a recent innovation, and there remains some controversy in the fire protection profession regarding the applications for which they are suitable. Carbon monoxide fire detectors are not, by definition, equivalent to smoke detectors. They respond to the carbon monoxide produced when the rate of burning is limited by the supply of oxygen. A freely burning fire in a very plentiful supply of oxygen would not produce a great deal of carbon monoxide. It should also be noted that carbon monoxide fire detectors are not the same as the carbon monoxide gas detectors used in dwellings to detect carbon monoxide from inefficient fuel burning appliances. The latter devices either operate at too high a carbon monoxide level and/or incorporate too long a time delay, to give early warning of fire. While, at the time of writing, there is no British, European or International standard for carbon monoxide fire detectors, in order to enable their use in appropriate circumstances, BS 5839-6 recommends compliance with a test standard published by the Loss Prevention Certification Board (as their standard, LPS 1265).

A potential benefit of carbon monoxide fire detectors is that they are likely to be immune to a number of the most common environmental influences that cause false alarms from smoke detectors, such as dust, steam, cigarette smoke, and many fumes produced in kitchens, such as those resulting from making toast. They are, however, sensitive to many types of smouldering fire and fires in which the rate of burning is controlled by the supply of air. Arguably, these are the most likely types of fire to occur in a dwelling.

Perhaps, in a domestic environment, the greatest disadvantage of a carbon monoxide fire detector is that the electrochemical cell, which is used as the sensor within a carbon monoxide fire detector, has a finite life, after which replacement is necessary. The Code advises that this life is, typically, seven years. On this basis, the Code stresses the need for owners and occupiers of dwellings to understand the need for replacement of electrochemical cells in any carbon monoxide fire detectors.

The Code suggests that carbon monoxide fire detectors might not be suitable for dwellings, unless the detectors are incorporated in a system that is likely to be subject to periodic maintenance for the entire life of the system. More specifically, the Code recommends that carbon monoxide fire detectors should not be used within dwellings unless they are incorporated within a Grade A, B or C system and there is a high likelihood that the system will be subject to periodic maintenance by a competent person at periods not exceeding 12 months, or, alternatively, unless a fault warning is given to indicate the need to replace the electrochemical cell of the detector before it reaches the end of its anticipated life. While the latter fault warning arrangement is not normal, there is no reason why such a facility could not be incorporated within a carbon monoxide fire detector.

Subject to the above, the Code accepts the provision of carbon monoxide fire detectors within the circulation areas of dwellings, provided there is also an equal number of optical smoke detectors. Thus, for example, in a large dwelling with long corridors, it might be acceptable to alternate carbon monoxide and optical smoke detectors along the corridor. In this connection, it has been claimed that carbon monoxide fire detectors in corridors can give an earlier warning of fire in an adjacent room than optical smoke detectors, although this claim remains controversial. More generally, as a rule of thumb, the Code suggests that if, in any room of a dwelling, a heat detector could give adequate fire protection, a carbon monoxide detector could be used. This would not, however, apply to kitchens, as false alarms might result from poor ventilation and dirty, inefficient gas burning appliances.

The Code also recognizes the potential benefits of multi-sensor fire detection systems. Multi-sensor detectors tend only to be found in the large, sophisticated fire detection and alarm systems found in very large properties. In some cases, the reason that more than one sensor (i.e. heat, smoke or carbon monoxide sensors) are incorporated within one detector head is to provide a response to a broader spectrum of fires. Thus, for this purpose, a heat sensor can be incorporated within the same detector as an optical smoke sensor or a carbon monoxide fire sensor.

Usually, the sensors in a multi-sensor fire detection system do not operate independently, but the software of the system uses the multiple signals to interpret, for example, whether the signals from the sensors are indicative of a fire or a false alarm. Accordingly, appropriately designed multi-sensor fire detection systems can be more immune to false alarms than traditional fire detection systems. As far as the Code is concerned, if a multi-sensor detector satisfies the appropriate requirements for a smoke detector (i.e. the requirements of BS EN 54-7), it may be used in any circumstances in which the use of a smoke detector would provide adequate fire protection. However, if one of the sensors is a carbon monoxide sensor, the limitations regarding the Grade of system and the requirement for periodic maintenance, applicable to carbon monoxide fire detectors, apply. Also, if a multi-sensor fire detector incorporates an ionization chamber smoke sensor, it should only be used in circulation areas into which kitchens open if the system incorporates suitable measures to limit the potential for false alarms during cooking processes.

13. Location and siting of detectors

How many and where?

Much of the guidance in clause 11 of the Code, which deals with location and siting of detectors, simply reflects what has become well-recognized good practice. For an existing simple single-storey dwelling, a minimum standard of protection (Category LD3 system) comprises a single smoke alarm, sited as close as possible to the living accommodation. In existing multi-storey dwellings, there should be at least one smoke detector per floor in the Category LD3 system recommended by the Code. However, as discussed in an earlier chapter, the Code recommends that new dwellings, existing dwellings of four or more storeys comprising no more than 200 m^2 floor area on any floor, and existing two- or more storey dwellings with more than 200 m^2 area on any floor, should be protected by a Category LD2 system, with additional heat detectors in every kitchen and the principal habitable room. (If more than one room might be used as the principal habitable room, a heat detector should be installed in each of these rooms.)

In the circulation spaces, additional detectors should be installed if necessary to ensure that no point is further than 7.5 m from the nearest smoke detector. Similarly, within rooms protected by detectors, no point should be further than 7.5 m from the nearest smoke detector, or 5.3 m from the nearest heat detector if the room is protected by heat detectors. Where smoke alarms are installed, additional smoke alarms may also be necessary to ensure adequate audibility throughout the house and, in particular, a sound level of 85 dB(A) at each bedroom door. (The subject of alarm audibility is discussed in a later chapter.)

Other specific guidance on siting detectors comprises the following simple recommendations:

- In multi-storey dwellings, at least one detector should be located on the ground floor between each staircase and every room, other than a toilet, bathroom or shower room. Where rooms are located on both sides of a staircase, a smoke detector should be sited mid-way between the doors to these rooms. A further detector(s) should be located on each main landing.
- At least one detector should be located between every bedroom and every other room in the dwelling, other than a toilet, bathroom or shower room. Where such rooms are located on both sides of any bedroom, a smoke detector should be sited mid-way between the doors to these rooms.
- An open plan living room or dining room (or any other room in which fire might start) containing a staircase should be treated as a circulation area. It should, therefore, be protected by at least one smoke detector.

Mounting positions

Although there is sometimes a tendency to regard ceiling and wall mounting as direct alternatives, the Code expresses a preference for ceiling mounting, as this is the most efficient means of exposing detectors to the smoke and hot gases produced by a fire. Because, close to walls, there is a relatively dead area for the transport of smoke, the Code recommends that detectors should not be mounted closer than 300 mm to walls.

Light fittings can also affect smoke flow due either to the size and shape of the fitting or to thermal effects. Accordingly, the Code recommends that detectors are not located closer than 300 mm horizontally to any light fitting unless there is test evidence to prove that the proximity of the light fitting will not adversely affect the efficiency of the detector.

The reason for this last caveat is that some available mains-operated smoke alarms (with battery backup) are designed to form part of a light fitting. This concept is interesting because it enables a smoke alarm to be unobtrusively sited in what is often a suitably centrally located position on a ceiling. The light switch can also serve as a test and silence control. No code of practice should act as an unnecessary obstacle to the use of new systems or novel ideas. Provided such systems can be shown by test to be unaffected by their mounting position, and other recommendations of the Code are satisfied, the recommendations of the Code regarding distance of detectors from light fittings do not present an obstacle to their use.

The Code adopts the advice in BS 5839-1 that ceiling-mounted detectors should be located so that their sensitive elements are between 25 mm and 150 mm below the ceiling in the case of heat detectors, and between 25 mm and 600 mm below in the case of smoke detectors. This is absolutely conventional practice and need not be discussed further.

However, the Code accepts that ceiling mounting may prove impracticable. The term 'impracticable' is not defined, but this could presumably relate to a wide range of circumstances from difficulties in obtaining a straightforward cable route to the presence of very high ceilings that could make access to detectors difficult. Under the above circumstances, the Code states that detectors may be wall mounted, provided that the room or hallway does not exceed 10 m in length or breadth and that the floor area of the protected space does not exceed 50 m^2.

If wall mounting is to be adopted, the Code recommends only the use of detectors that the manufacturers' instructions state are suitable for wall mounting. (The manufacturer may be opposed to this if, for example, the design of the detector were such that the collection of dust on certain surfaces within the detector could cause the detector to malfunction.) The Code also recommends that wall mounted detectors are located such that the detection element is between 150 mm and 300 mm below the ceiling, so avoiding the dead space at the ceiling/wall junction, but still lying within the hot gas layer. In order to ensure that the detector is not mounted below the height of hot gases issuing from the top of a doorway, the Code recommends that the bottom of the detection element of any wall mounted detector is above the level of any door opening.

In order to ensure that detection of fire is not affected by air currents, the Code states that detectors should not be mounted adjacent to, or directly above, heaters or air conditioning vents. In mounting detectors, consideration should also be given to accessibility, for instance. The Code advises that this consideration is particularly important in the case of smoke alarms that incorporate a battery, or that have a test or alarm silence control, to which, of course, the occupier will need reasonably ready access. A particular location to avoid is immediately over a stairwell, where accessing the detector may be hazardous for the householder.

Although certain of the above guidance refers specifically to smoke detectors, the Code advises that, if carbon monoxide fire detectors are used, the location and siting of these detectors should comply with the recommendations for the location and siting of smoke detectors. However, restrictions in the use of carbon monoxide fire detectors, discussed in chapter 10, should be noted.

14. Limitation of false alarms

For many years, false alarms have plagued users of automatic fire detection and alarm systems, and although, in the large systems market, technological advances have contributed to some limitation of false alarms, the frequency of false alarms remains a serious problem for a significant number of users. Domestic fire detection systems produce a significantly higher rate of false alarms than most systems installed in industrial or commercial premises. In the latter premises, false alarms cause disruption to business, complacency of occupants to fire alarm signals and, often, unnecessary summoning of the fire service. In dwellings, the main effect of false alarms is irritation of occupants, sometimes to an extent that the fire detection is disabled either temporarily or permanently. Thus, false alarms are often extremely detrimental to the fire safety of occupants. As discussed later in this chapter, unnecessary summoning of the fire service to false alarms in dwellings is also beginning to become a problem.

The Code regards any fire signal that results from a cause other than fire as a false alarm. However, false alarms are sub-divided, in the Code, into four categories, recognizing that most false alarms do not result from faults in equipment. The four categories are defined as follows:

a) *Unwanted alarms*, in which a system has responded, either as designed or as the technology may reasonably be expected to respond, to any of the following:
    - a fire-like phenomenon or environmental influence (e.g. smoke from a nearby bonfire, dust or insects, processes that produce smoke or flame, or environmental effects that can render certain types of detector unstable, such as rapid air flow);
    - accidental damage;
    - inappropriate human action (e.g. operation of a system for test or maintenance purposes without prior warning to building occupants and/or an alarm receiving centre).

b) *Equipment false alarms*, in which the false alarm has resulted from a fault in the system.
c) *Malicious false alarms*, in which a person operates a manual call point or causes a fire detector to initiate a fire signal, whilst knowing that there is no fire.
d) *False alarms with good intent*, in which a person operates a manual call point or otherwise initiates a fire signal in the belief that there is a fire, when no fire actually exists.

The majority of false alarms in dwellings are 'unwanted alarms'; the Code lists the most common causes of unwanted alarms in dwellings, which are:

- fumes from cooking processes (including toasting of bread);
- steam (from bathrooms, shower rooms and kitchens);
- tobacco smoke;
- dust (whether built up over a period of time or generated while cleaning);
- insects;
- aerosol spray (e.g. deodorants and cleaning fluids);
- smoke from sources other than a fire in the building (e.g. from an external bonfire);
- 'hot work', such as burning off paintwork with a blowlamp;
- processes that produce smoke or flame (e.g. flambéing of food);
- incense;
- candles;
- high humidity;
- water ingress.

The Code notes that most unwanted alarms occur during cooking activities. It is for this reason that, as discussed in chapter 12, the Code stresses that optical smoke detectors are much more suitable than ionization chamber smoke detectors for installation in hallways and circulation spaces into which kitchens open. It is a specific recommendation of the Code that all smoke detectors within areas, such as hallways and corridors, into which kitchens open, should be of the optical type, unless there are overriding considerations that preclude the use of optical smoke detectors; such circumstances do not commonly occur. In a typical two-storey house, the effect of this recommendation is that the two detectors installed in the circulation areas (i.e. on the upstairs landing and the ground floor hallway) should both be of the optical type.

It is sometimes argued that there is no harm in an arrangement whereby the detector in the ground floor hallway is of the optical type, while the detector on the upstairs landing is of the ionization chamber type. The argument in favour of this arrangement is that, from a fire detection point of view, it offers the potential for the earliest detection of fire since, according to the nature of the fire, one of the two types of detector might operate before the other. It should also be noted that the Code recommends against the siting of optical smoke detectors in close proximity to rooms from which steam may issue, such as poorly ventilated bathrooms, shower rooms and certain kitchens. As the bathroom in a two-storey house is normally upstairs, the latter recommendation would, indeed, be satisfied by installation of an ionization chamber detector on the upstairs landing.

Nevertheless, natural convection currents, particularly on hot days, are likely to transport fumes from a downstairs kitchen to an upstairs ionization chamber smoke detector. Accordingly, such is the importance now attributed by BS 5839-6 to the avoidance of false alarms, the use of an ionization chamber smoke detector within the circulation space of a normal-size house would be a variation from the recommendations of the Code, unless there was some good reason that an optical smoke detector could not be used.

As discussed in chapter 12, the above recommendations endeavour to reverse current custom and practice in respect of the common use of ionization chamber smoke alarms in dwellings. Ionization chamber smoke detectors could, nevertheless, be used in certain individual rooms. Ionization chamber smoke detectors are also less likely to produce false alarms in dusty spaces, such as roof voids, where they should be used in preference to optical smoke detectors. Similarly, if dense tobacco smoke is likely to occur in a room, any smoke detector used in that room should be of the ionization chamber type, unless there are overriding considerations to the contrary.

More generally, the Code recommends that no fire detectors, of any type, should be installed in bathrooms and shower rooms. In these areas, ingress of moisture would be likely to cause false alarms. Also, in kitchens, only heat detectors should be used. In other rooms within a dwelling, the Code recommends that, before smoke detectors are specified, it should be confirmed that their use is necessary in order to satisfy the objectives of the system, based on, for example, a fire risk assessment.

This is a simple acknowledgement of the fact that the more smoke detectors there are in a dwelling, the greater the number of false alarms that are likely to occur. Indeed, the number of false alarms from any dwelling is likely to be more or less directly proportional to the number of smoke detectors in the dwelling. This advice is consistent with the advice in the Code that, in new dwellings, heat detectors should be installed in each kitchen and principal habitable room, even though, obviously, smoke detectors would give an earlier warning and therefore a higher standard of protection. Heat detectors rarely produce false alarms, but, if heat detectors are used in rooms, there is a need to accept the fact that there will be a relatively large fire before a warning is given.

In the early 1980s, the analogue fire detection system was hailed as the answer to false alarms. In analogue systems, the fire detectors themselves do not make the decision as to whether or not there is a fire, but instead merely transmit information about their environment to the control equipment, which can analyse the data and attempt to filter out signals that are not representative of fire. Even in the simplest analogue systems, a 'pre-warning' can often be given when the measured value of temperature, smoke-like particle density, etc. rises, so resulting in the avoidance of a potential false alarm. Such systems are now used in most non-domestic premises, other than small buildings, in which 'conventional' systems are still commonly used. However, they are unlikely to be found in dwellings other than HMOs, sheltered housing schemes or large mansions. Nevertheless, the Code recommends that, in very large properties, in which more than 50 detectors are necessary, only systems of the analogue type should be used.

In the future, the use of multi-sensor fire detection systems, in which each detector contains more than one sensor type, may make an even more significant impact on false alarms. Accordingly, the Code notes that, in these very large properties, if there is potential for a high rate of false alarms, consideration could be given to the use of certain multi-sensor systems, with detection algorithms that are intended to minimize the occurrence of false alarms.

In some large mansions and historic houses, aspirating fire detection systems are used. The reason for this is to provide 'invisible' fire detection. The pipework of the aspirating system can be concealed within a floor void, from which short capillary tubes can be dropped through a hole in the ceiling to provide detection on the floor below. However, most aspirating fire detection systems are intended to provide much higher sensitivity to smoke than conventional point detectors, as they were originally designed to provide very early warning of fire in critical electronic equipment rooms, such as computer suites, in which there is a very clean environment. The Code points out that such high sensitivity is not necessarily required in a dwelling. In such cases, the Code effectively recommends that the sensitivity of the system be 'de-tuned', so that the system provides a sensitivity that is only equivalent to that of point detectors conforming to BS EN 54-7[8]. It

---

[8] BS EN 54-7: 2001. *Fire detection and fire alarm systems – Smoke detectors – Point detectors using scattered light, transmitted light or ionization.*

should be noted that not all aspirating fire detection systems can provide this 'normal' sensitivity.

As discussed in a previous chapter, high levels of false alarms sometimes occur in HMOs, simply because of the number of occupants, each of whom carry out activities, such as cooking, that can lead to false alarms. In many types of HMO, the risk to occupants from fire is greater than that in a single-family dwelling, but occupants sometimes disable the fire detection and alarm system as a result of the nuisance caused by false alarms. A very effective solution to this problem is the use of mixed systems, which were discussed in chapter 10.

However, in clause 12, the Code also recognizes an alternative solution for large HMOs. In this arrangement, subject to the agreement of the enforcing authority, a short time delay (of typically no more than two minutes) is incorporated between operation of a smoke detector in one dwelling and a fire alarm signal in other dwellings units, but an immediate alarm is given in the dwelling in which the smoke detector operates. If, during the delay period, the system is reset, no alarm signal is then given in other dwelling units. The Code notes that a reset control could actually be installed in each dwelling unit, provided that it only resets alarm signals generated within that unit and occupants are given clear instruction regarding procedures for the use of the control.

This arrangement satisfies the two principal objectives for fire detection in houses in multiple occupation discussed in chapter 10. Occupants are given an immediate warning of a fire in their own dwelling, but can prevent their false alarms from affecting their neighbours. This pre-supposes, of course, that the dwelling is occupied at the time of the false alarm and that occupants can respond quickly enough. Nevertheless, in practice, most false alarms are of the unwanted alarm type and occur when occupants are present, as a result of the occupants' activities. Moreover, in the size of dwelling unit normally found in an HMO, two minutes would usually be sufficient time for occupants to determine that a fire alarm signal was a false alarm. The advantage of this arrangement, which, at the time of writing, is extremely uncommon and can only be facilitated by a small number of proprietary systems, is that it involves only a single fire detection and alarm system that will be designed in accordance with BS 5839-1, rather than the use of any smoke alarms.

Even if great care is taken in installation design and use of a dwelling, it is implicitly acknowledged in the Code that false alarms are bound to occur. It might even be asserted that the system that produces no false alarms is probably incapable of detection of a fire. For this reason, the Code gives considerable attention to the need for facilities whereby audible alarm signals that result from unwanted alarms and equipment false alarms can be silenced. These measures were discussed in chapter 11.

Traditionally, other than in very expensive properties in which fire detection has been installed to protect the property (often as a result of insurers' requirements), the only real effect of false alarms was disturbance to occupants. Only rarely were fire services summoned to false alarms in dwellings. However, within the last few years, automatic transmission of fire alarm signals from fire alarm systems in dwellings to alarm receiving centres, from where the fire service is summoned, have become much more common. Often, this arises from the use of Grade C systems, comprising intruder alarm systems, to which a number of smoke detectors are connected. Since automatic transmission of intruder alarm signals to an alarm receiving centre is common practice, it is then very easy to use a spare channel of the transmission equipment to transmit fire alarm signals as well. Alternatively, if a property is provided with an intruder alarm system that has remote transmission facilities, it is also simple to connect a completely separate fire alarm system to the alarm transmission equipment, again using a spare channel to transmit fire alarm signals.

Already, the practices described above are resulting in a noticeable increase in the number of false alarms in dwellings to which fire services are summoned. If the practice continues to grow, as seems likely, the effect will be a significant increase in the false alarms to which fire services are summoned, given the relatively high rate of false alarms in many dwellings. Accordingly, the Code virtually discourages the transmission of fire alarm signals from fire detection and alarm systems in dwellings to the fire service, at least without very careful consideration. Clause 12.2 of the Code recommends that, other than in the case of sheltered housing, automatic transmission of fire alarm signals to an alarm receiving centre (or direct to the fire service) should not be specified for a fire detection and alarm system in a dwelling, unless the specifier has confirmed that such a facility is necessary in order to satisfy the objectives of the system. The most obvious possible objective is property protection, and it is anticipated that large, high value properties will still have this facility, which is often a requirement of the fire insurer. Another possible objective noted in the Code is protection of occupants at special risk from fire; this might include people with severe disabilities.

Equally, notwithstanding the recommendations of the Code, many householders will, no doubt, be sold this facility by alarm system installers, and it is difficult to suggest that a householder has no right to such a facility. Accordingly, the Code recommends that, where automatic transmission facilities are provided, they should comply with various recommendations in clause 20 of the Code, which specifically addresses remote transmission of alarm signals. These measures are discussed in chapter 22. It should also be noted that, in clause 12, the Code recommends that, before remote monitoring of fire alarm signals is put in place, occupiers should be given formal, written instructions regarding the need to avoid transmission of false alarms to the fire service and appropriate means whereby such false alarms can be avoided. A sample of appropriate written guidance is contained in Annex D to the Code.

15. The audible fire alarm signal: audibility and other characteristics

Although most of our concern so far in this Guide has related to fire protection philosophy and system engineering, the simple fact is that, if the alarm sound cannot be heard or does not rouse people from sleep, all the philosophy and engineering will have been wasted; the alarm system will not serve its purpose and people may die as a result. Clause 13 of the Code advises on the alarm devices that should be used and the audibility that should be achieved.

Alarm audibility is a particularly difficult area for both the Code writer and the system designer. Prior to 1980, life was somewhat simpler, in that fire alarm codes of practice, applicable to non-domestic premises, simply demanded that the fire alarm signal should be audible. This permitted a great deal of flexibility, but, of course, introduced a similar measure of subjectivity.

Since 1980, BS 5839-1 has provided objective guidance in the form of the sound pressure levels that should be achieved in the building. The minimum sound pressure level generally specified in BS 5839-1 is 65 dB(A) – the (A) reference means that the sound level meter should be set to the A weighting, which roughly weights different frequencies in accordance with the varying sensitivity of the human ear to varying frequencies. However, BS 5839-1 openly acknowledges that this figure is rather arbitrary, and a lower sound pressure level, of 60 dB(A), is accepted in limited areas. Where background noise is likely to be more than 60 dB(A), BS 5839-1 recommends that the sound pressure level should be at least 5 dB above background.

Most important of all, however, BS 5839-1 advises that, if the alarm signal is intended to wake people from sleep, a sound pressure level of 75 dB(A) should be achieved at the bedhead. Even though this is quite a high sound level, it is accepted that there is no guarantee that every person will be awakened by it, particularly if they are under the influence of alcohol or drugs. In fact, the figure was selected as long ago as 1980 on the basis that, in research carried out in the USA during the 1970s, this figure was found to be sufficient to arouse 90% of university students from sleep. History does not record the state of these sleeping students in 1970s America!

For the designer, achieving these levels can be difficult, and it is often costly to provide and install the number of sounders required. Bells tend to produce something in excess of 90 dB(A) at a range of 1 m. Most electronic sounders produce just over 100 dB(A) at the same range, although higher output devices can produce 115 dB(A). However, because the decibel scale is logarithmic, as the distance from the sounder doubles, in theory the sound pressure level decreases by 6 dB. In practice, because of reflections, this inverse square law does not always apply, but this will depend on the nature of linings and furnishings.

However, most of the problems in achieving adequate audibility in any fire alarm system arise from attenuation of the sound by walls, partitions and doors. The practicalities are such that 65 dB(A) cannot usually be achieved if there is more than one door between the area in question and the nearest sounder. Even a single door, particularly a solid fire resisting door, will usually attenuate sound sufficiently to prevent 75 dB(A) from being achieved at the bedhead unless the sounder is actually within the bedroom.

All the above considerations relate to BS 5839-1 and fire alarm systems in any type of building. What is their relevance to BS 5839-6? Well, in drafting Part 6, it would have been very easy and perfectly logical to lift the guidance straight from Part 1. After all, if it takes 65 dB(A) to enable people to hear the fire alarm signal in an office building, surely it takes no less to make the family hear it whilst they are squabbling over what to watch on a television set that is producing a similar or higher level at their ears (my family anyway)! Moreover, if it takes 75 dB(A) to wake the same family while on holiday in a boarding house, why should it take any less to wake them in their own home?

These are compelling arguments that can be countered only on the basis of current custom and practice, practicality and, ultimately, it must be admitted, cost. Current practice, when BS 5839-6 was first drafted, was to install no more than one smoke alarm on each floor of a traditional two-storey house. The relevant manufacturing standard, BS 5446-1, required that these smoke alarms produce no less than 85 dB(A) at a distance of 3 m. Guidance that supported building regulations (e.g. in England and Wales, Approved Document B under the Building Regulations) specified that there should be a smoke alarm within 3 m of bedroom doors. This requirement was related to the audibility of the alarm for occupants of the bedroom, rather than detection of fire.

Even in the case of two interlinked smoke alarms, the extent to which the sound from one reinforces the sound of the other will be negligible. Basically, the sound level achieved over most areas will simply be that produced by the nearer smoke alarm. Even allowing for some reinforcement of sound due to reflections from hard surfaces, it cannot be assumed that smoke alarms installed in accordance with previous guidance would achieve more than 85 dB(A) at the doorway to any bedroom. In new dwellings, the interlinked heat alarms in the kitchen and lounge will add virtually nothing to the sound pressure level in any bedroom.

Relatively thin, but reasonably well fitting, domestic doors will attenuate sound by around 20 dB. Therefore, it is most unlikely that, in houses protected by smoke alarms, sound levels of anything like 75 dB(A) are achieved at bedheads when bedroom doors are closed. Yet, notwithstanding quite extensive enquiries in 1994, and again in 2003, no one has been able to present the BSI Committee with any significant evidence that there is a real problem of people dying or being seriously injured in dwellings because they did not hear their smoke alarm; quite the contrary, there is evidence that people have been roused from sleep. The general impression is that, often, where people have failed to hear the smoke alarm, siting did not satisfy recognized good practice, or those involved may have been under the influence of alcohol or drugs and so may not have been roused by even higher levels, such as 75 dB(A).

In the USA, in 2003, local television stations in several cities carried out demonstrations to show that sleeping children do not always wake up when a smoke alarm operates. The NFPA have responded to this by announcing that their Fire Protection Research Foundation are considering further research on the subject. In the meantime, the NFPA have advised parents to consider whether their children will wake up when a smoke alarm operates and, if not, to ensure that their 'fire safety plan' addresses this. NFPA statistics certainly show that smoke alarms are nearly as effective in saving the lives of 6 to 10 year old children as in saving the lives of the other age groups. The NFPA admit that they do not know whether this is simply the result of parental action to rouse children.

However, other research appears to confirm the results of the demonstrations in the USA. In Australia, research by Victoria University had already shown that children under the age of 15 were likely to sleep through the sound of a smoke alarm operating. In another eight-month study with elementary school children in the USA, the same finding resulted. As a result, Underwriters' Laboratories in the USA, who test and approve fire protection products, including smoke alarms, and the United States Consumer Product Safety Commission have promised to investigate the issue.

On the other hand, there would be practical difficulties in achieving 75 dB(A) with any reliability in any room within an average dwelling. It would necessitate a smoke alarm or alarm sounder within each room in question. In a three-bedroom house, there would be a need to increase the typical number of smoke alarms used from two to five. There is no doubt that this would represent an enhanced standard of protection, but, given the absence of any evidence of widespread problems, the additional costs would be difficult to justify.

Perhaps it might have been possible for BS 5839-6 to recommend just one additional smoke alarm in, say, the bedroom used by the parents but, if 75 dB(A) were really essential, this would not have been satisfactory due to difficulties in defining the bedroom involved. Moreover, there can be no guarantee that, whenever the house is occupied, there will be persons occupying any one bedroom. In practice, it was necessary to 'bite the bullet' and make a decision as to whether all bedrooms or none need have smoke alarms in order to provide the minimum acceptable standard of safety. However, the Code does make the point that it is essential for the system to be capable of rousing the principal occupants, and gives the example of the adult occupants in a single-family dwelling. Overall, the position taken in the drafting of BS 5839-6: 2004 is that there is no real justification for a suggestion that, in all dwellings, bedrooms should be fitted with smoke alarms in order to ensure occupants would be roused from sleep in the event of fire.

The fundamental recommendation in BS 5839-6 is that a Category LD system should either be capable of producing at least 85 dB(A) at the doorway to each bedroom (with the door open), irrespective of where fire is detected, or have a sounder (or smoke alarm) within the bedroom that will operate regardless of where fire is detected. If smoke alarms, or other commonly used fire alarm sounders, are located within 3 m of each bedroom door, this recommendation is almost certain to be satisfied. Moreover, a very small shortfall of 1 to 2 dB below the recommended 85 dB(A) might be regarded as an acceptable variation.

The recommendation in the standard refers to the level measured in the open doorway, but, of course, doors vary in their thickness, construction and so attenuation. The sound pressure level that actually occurs at any bedhead will, therefore, vary from one dwelling to another. If the door to a bedroom is fire resisting, it will tend to attentuate sound significantly more than a hollow domestic door. Even the latter doors are likely to attentuate sound by around 20 dB. Thus, actual sound pressure levels at the bedhead in a bedroom, when the bedroom door is shut, are likely to be around 55 to 65dB(A).

Does this mean that the 75 dB(A) specified in BS 5839-1 is 'wrong'? Not necessarily. The clear intent is that the guidance in Part 6 should not in any way undermine the guidance in Part 1. Indeed, the Code suggests that the difference between dwellings and, say, hotels is that, in their own homes, people can possibly be roused by an unusual sound of relatively low level. In premises with which they are unfamiliar, higher sound levels might be required.

This is probably just a convenient way of warning people that they should not attempt to use the recommendations of BS 5839-6 to dilute the recommendations of BS 5839-1 in respect of audibility. In truth, the whole subject of sound levels required to wake people from sleep is much more complicated than would be suggested by reading either Code. When one discusses the matter with eminent specialists in the field of sleep research, they sometimes express surprise that 75 dB(A) is deemed to be necessary. It has been pointed out to me by one such expert that, if 75 dB(A) were required, most of the world's infants would starve while their mothers slept blissfully through their cries of hunger!

The point is that, even while someone is asleep, their brain recognizes sounds that require them to respond. Such sounds can, I am assured, rouse people at quite low sound levels, compared with the level of general background noise, such as that caused by traffic, that would be required to wake them. Perhaps then this is indeed the justification for the lower sound levels in Part 6 – everyone should recognize the sound of their own fire alarm system and subconsciously appreciate the need for urgent response! The problem of arousing young children from sleep may well, therefore, be that they have not yet developed the subconscious response to sounds of an emergency when they are asleep that would occur in the case of a responsible adult.

When the first draft of BS 5839-6: 1995 was published in 1994, there was some concern by environmental health officers that a departure from the traditional 75 dB(A) might increase the risks to occupants of HMOs. In some of these premises, it was felt that ambient noise levels from neighbours can sometimes be high and that quite high sound levels can be required to wake people.

While there has to be some sympathy with this view, account has to be taken of the practicalities of installing a sounder in every bedroom of an HMO, when perhaps the money might be better spent on enhancing other fire precautions, bearing in mind that, in purpose built flats, a different recommendation would apply. Moreover, if the 'mixed systems' concept were applied (see chapter 10), the occupant of a self-contained flat within an HMO could end up with an alarm sounder and a smoke alarm in the hallway, plus an alarm sounder and a smoke alarm in every bedroom!

Again, the BSI committee have opted for flexibility. The Code suggests that the above recommendations on sound pressure level apply to many HMOs of limited size and with straightforward escape. However, the Code also notes that, in some HMOs, ambient noise levels or other factors might justify the local authority in requiring 75 dB(A) at the bedhead in every bedroom, particularly in the event of a fire *in an area outside that dwelling unit* (author's italics). The Code recommends that the need for this significantly higher sound pressure level within any or all bedrooms should be determined as part of a fire risk assessment. The Code notes that this risk assessment might determine that the 75 dB(A) is needed only in certain bedrooms.

This compromise enables an enforcing authority to demand 75 dB(A) at every bedhead if they really believe this is necessary to ensure the safety of occupants. On the other hand, the environmental health officer should not feel exposed if he or she decides to accept the 85 dB(A) at the doorway recommended in the Code. Equally, if an enforcing authority or specifier does want the 75 dB(A) to be achieved in any or all bedrooms, it will be necessary for this to be made clear in the enforcement notice, specification, etc. Otherwise, the default level of 85 dB(A) at the bedroom doorway would apply if the requirement were only compliance with BS 5839-6. Further flexibility is implied in the words in italics in the paragraph above. This implies that, in the 'mixed systems' concept, even if a bell were installed in each bedroom to warn of detection of fire by the Grade A system covering the escape routes, a single smoke alarm in the hallway of each dwelling unit might prove sufficient, albeit that this would be designed to achieve 85 dB(A) at the doorway, as opposed to 75 dB(A) at the bedhead.

In terms of audibility, the Code concentrates on bedrooms. It makes no recommendations as to the minimum sound pressure level in other areas of the house. The only recommendation for these areas is that, in all areas in which it is necessary to provide a warning, occupants are likely to be able to hear the alarm under most foreseeable circumstances. In many cases, this will, no doubt, apply to all areas of the house. On the other hand, perhaps, say, a conservatory with doors opening directly to the open air might not be an area in which it is necessary to provide a warning to the single occupant of the dwelling. Note also the use of the term 'under most foreseeable circumstances'. When I play my drum kit or play loud rock music, no sounder on Earth would be audible! Again, a matter for thought, judgement and, in the end, reasonableness. The Code suggests that, in practice, the areas in which it is necessary to provide a warning might be determined as part of a fire risk assessment.

In order to maximize the sound levels from smoke alarms, the Code acknowledges that all smoke alarms should ideally be interlinked. (In Grades

A, B and C systems, the Code recommends that all sounders should operate simultaneously, regardless of where fire is detected.) This is categorically recommended in the case of all new dwellings, all HMOs (other than houses with long-term lodgers and houses shared by no more than six persons), all rented maisonettes and rented two- or more storey houses and all houses of three or more storeys. The Code notes that interlinking is also preferable in all other houses, and it is specifically recommended that this advice be incorporated in instructions to householders (e.g. within the smoke alarm instructions). The Code stops short of a positive recommendation in respect of these lower risk houses, however, simply because in the case of those retrofitted by householders, the advice is unlikely to be well-accepted.

With regard to the alarm devices themselves, the Code accepts any reliable form of alarm device, whether combined with a detector in the form of a smoke alarm or as a discrete device such as an electronic sounder or bell.

Where separate alarm sounders are used, the type of sound is largely a matter for personal taste. However, the sound output of an electronic sounder, when measured along the axis of the sounder, is generally higher than the output of a bell. Nevertheless, electronic sounders tend to be much more directional, and the output can fall off by as much as, say, around 10 dB at right angles to the sounder. This is, of course, assuming no reflections from walls, which will tend to reduce the directional effect.

BS 5839-1 recommends that fire alarm sounder frequencies should ideally be in the range 500 Hz–1,000 Hz. This advice is reiterated in BS 5839-6. Higher frequencies will be more attenuated by construction (which is why when the neighbours play loud rock music it sounds mostly like bass and drums). Age and hearing damage also reduce the response of the human ear to high frequencies.

Unfortunately, most smoke alarms produce frequencies well above the recommended frequency range. This is recognized in the Code, which limits the frequency produced by smoke alarms and heat alarms to 3,500 Hz. However, for the reasons given above, this frequency is really higher than desirable. It has been known for those with hearing difficulties to require visual alarms, because the high frequency produced by their smoke alarms was difficult to hear. The low current high frequency piezoelectric devices used in smoke alarms were selected by the industry as they are cheap and draw only low current. Regrettably, there is probably not a ready alternative.

To prevent confusion of occupants, the Code recommends that fire warning signals are distinguishable from those produced by any other alarm system in the dwelling. Obvious examples of such other alarm systems are intruder alarm systems and carbon monoxide gas detectors.

16. Fire alarm warnings for deaf and hard of hearing people

Products for use in both domestic and commercial properties to warn deaf people in the event of fire have been available for some years. However, until very recently there were no standards for these products, nor was there any recognized guidance on the use and installation of the products. The first step forward in this respect occurred with the revision of BS 5839-1 in 2002. Included in the 2002 version is a clause giving recommendations for means of giving warning to deaf and hard of hearing people in the event of fire. BS 5839-1 is, nevertheless, a code of practice and not a standard for products. Accordingly, although BS 5839-1 acknowledges the use of flashing beacons and vibrating devices as a means of warning deaf and hard of hearing people, and gives considerable advice on the use of 'portable alarm devices' (i.e. vibrating pagers), no performance requirements for relevant products are contained in BS 5839-1, other than in a normative Annex that sets out relevant recommendations for transmission equipment used in vibrating pager systems.

In general, of course, the recommendations of BS 5839-1 are not applicable to fire detection and alarm systems in normal dwellings, which are, typically, protected by the use of smoke alarms, rather than the systems described in BS 5839-1. For deaf and hard of hearing people, there has, therefore, been something of an inequality. People with normal hearing have, for many years, been able to go to virtually any D-I-Y outlet and select one or more suitable smoke alarms from a wide range of smoke alarms, all of which have normally been third-party certificated as compliant with BS 5446-1 and so, for example, bear the BSI 'Kitemark'. A range of equipment has been available for use by deaf and hard of hearing people, but they could not be given the same confidence in these products, as there was, until 2004, no standard against which they could be tested and third-party certificated.

Happily, this situation changed in 2004, with the publication of BS 5446-3[9]. This standard sets out requirements for smoke alarms, along with associated equipment, designed to warn deaf and hard of hearing people in dwellings in the event of fire. Therefore, in the same way as a person with normal hearing can obtain a 'box' that, when opened at home, contains everything necessary to provide a warning in the event of fire (i.e. the smoke alarm and associated instructions), a deaf or hard of hearing person can now purchase a similar (but larger!) 'box' or 'kit' that, when opened at home, contains all the hardware and instructions necessary to provide a fire warning system. BS 5446-3 contains requirements for the entire 'kit' and its contents.

As well as one or more smoke alarms, these kits contain flashing beacons as the primary means of giving warning and vibrating pads, which are placed under pillows or mattresses to rouse a deaf or hard of hearing person from sleep. The pads may be triggered by a hard-wired circuit or by radio. The 'kits' may, in addition, contain a vibrating pager, but this would be regarded as an optional extra as, in dwellings, it is not considered that a vibrating pager alone would be an adequately reliable means of warning a deaf or hard of hearing person; for example, there could be no guarantee that the pager would constantly be worn at all times when the deaf or hard of hearing person is within the dwelling. Clearly, however, it is important to select the right 'kit' for any deaf or hard of hearing person.

Care should also be taken to ensure equality between deaf or hard of hearing people and people with normal hearing in respect of system Grade. As discussed in chapter 7, the appropriate Grade of system for any person, regardless of their hearing capability, should either be based on the prescriptive table within the Code or on a fire risk assessment. Clearly, it would be inequitable to determine that one Grade of system was appropriate for a person with normal hearing, while another (perhaps cheaper) Grade would satisfy the needs for a deaf or hard of hearing person. Accordingly, the Code stresses the need to ensure that any fire warning system intended for warning deaf or hard of hearing people in the event of fire is of the appropriate Grade. The Code also makes the point that if, for example, a Grade A or Grade B system is appropriate for protection of occupants, it is not acceptable to install a lower Grade of system (e.g. one comprising smoke alarms), just because this would afford a cheaper form of warning system.

On the other hand, if a system comprising smoke alarms is an adequate form of fire detection and fire alarm system, a hearing impaired fire alarm kit conforming to the requirements of BS 5446-3 is specifically recommended by the Code, assuming that a special means of giving warning is necessary.

---

[9] BS 5446-3: 2004. *Fire detection and fire alarm devices for dwellings – Specification for smoke alarm kits for deaf and hard of hearing people.*

It is, therefore, necessary to take into account the individual needs of each deaf or hard of hearing person for whom the fire warning system is intended. Such 'tailor-made' consideration will also be necessary to determine the rooms and areas in the dwelling in which a warning needs to be given. The Code also points out that, in some cases, it might be appropriate to provide a means of warning a deaf or hard of hearing person when they are within, for example, the garden of the dwelling; a vibrating pager could be used for this purpose, provided its range is sufficient.

If smoke alarms are inappropriate, and a Grade A or Grade B system is necessary, the Code recommends that the system should then comply with clause 18 of BS 5839-1: 2002, which deals with means of giving warning to deaf or hard of hearing people when a system of the type to which BS 5839-1 applies is used. However, as noted above, BS 5839-1 does not set out performance requirements for alarm devices. Accordingly, the Code recommends that visual alarm devices, vibrating pads and vibrating pagers used in any Grade of system (including Grades A and B) should conform to the relevant requirements of BS 5446-3. This recommendation recognizes the value of the requirements of BS 5446-3 for these devices, regardless of the situation in which they are used. Thus, it is probably reasonable to assert that any visual alarm devices, vibrating pads and possibly even vibrating pagers, used in commercial properties (e.g. hotels) to warn deaf or hard of hearing people in the event of fire should also, at the very least, satisfy the relevant requirements of BS 5446-3.

17. Power supplies for the system

When, in an earlier chapter, the Grades of system were examined, it became clear that the Code recognizes two Grades of system (E and F) with a single source of supply (mains and battery power, respectively), while the remaining Grades, by definition, each have a main supply (derived from mains electricity) and a standby supply.

The Code now limits the use of systems with a single power supply. Thus, as discussed in chapter 9, in table 1 of the Code, which sets out the minimum recommended Grade of system for a wide range of dwellings, Grade E systems (mains-operated smoke alarms) are not specified as the minimum level of protection in any situation. Grade F systems (battery-operated smoke alarms) are deemed satisfactory for retrofitting in normal-size, existing, owner-occupied dwellings of up to two storeys, and in normal-size, existing rented flats and bungalows, but only if other fire precautions in these properties meet current standards. Obviously, therefore, Grade E systems could be used in these situations. Moreover, where Grade F is recommended, the Code also recommends that this be upgraded to Grade E if there is any doubt regarding the ability of the occupier to replace batteries in battery-operated smoke alarms soon after a low battery warning is given. On the other hand, the Grade F system should be upgraded to a Grade D system if there is a significant likelihood of the electricity supply being disconnected because the occupier is unable to pay for supplies.

In all situations other than those in which a Grade F system is deemed acceptable, the minimum Grade of system recommended in the Code is Grade D (or higher), in which there is a standby supply. In practice, a major cost factor in installing mains-operated smoke alarms is the labour cost. Accordingly, it might virtually be regarded as a false economy to install mains-operated smoke alarms without a standby supply, given the ability of those with a standby supply to continue to give protection at times of mains failure. For example, at the time of writing, if a contractor were installing smoke alarms in an estate of typical two-storey houses, the installed cost of mains-operated smoke alarms might be around £170, whereas the installed cost of mains-operated smoke alarms with a standby supply might be around £180. If the latter devices were connected to a lighting circuit (which would not be acceptable if the smoke alarms had no standby supply), the cost could actually fall to around, say, £125.

We also noted in an earlier chapter that we should talk about a standby supply, rather than a standby battery, since the Code recognizes capacitors as a suitable source of standby supply for smoke alarms. Capacitors cannot, at present, maintain smoke alarms in operation for anything like as long as a battery. On the other hand, they do have certain advantages. As a standby supply, they have the particular attraction that they should not need to be replaced periodically. They can also be recharged quite quickly, which could be a benefit in cases where occupants 'cycle' their electricity supplies by permitting pre-payment electricity meters to cut off supplies during times of day that they do not require electricity.

The Code recommends a 72 hour standby for all systems that have standby supplies. What is the basis of this figure? The answer is simple pragmatism. Firstly, it caters for the family who spend weekends away from home. If the power fails soon after they leave on a Friday night, even after their return on Sunday night they have all day on Monday to arrange for the fault to be rectified. Also, in the case of larger installations using Grade A or Grade B systems, it limits the physical size of the standby batteries to manageable proportions. However, even in the case of 72 hour standby, the lack of available space in modern control panels will often be such that a separate enclosure is required for the batteries.

In some respects, it is these larger systems that are the constraining factor, since the standby battery in a smoke alarm could power the smoke alarm for a much longer period than 72 hours. However, the Grades are, of course, defined in such a way that a requirement for one Grade of system can always be satisfied by a higher Grade of system; it would, therefore, have been inappropriate for the Code to call for a number of days standby for a Grade D system, but only 72 hour standby for a Grade A system.

Another practical factor to consider is the difficulty, in the case of systems using capacitors as the standby supply, to provide long periods of standby capacity. As is obvious from many of the Code's recommendations, the BSI committee have endeavoured not to eliminate the use of perfectly acceptable equipment unless there is very sound justification for so doing. The use of capacitors as a standby supply offers a number of advantages, albeit that their capacity is more limited than a battery. The 72 hour period specified in the Code should enable smoke alarms with capacitor standby supplies to be used.

Although the Code standardizes on a 72 hour standby for Grades A–D systems, it is accepted that, exceptionally, there may be cases where this is insufficient. Obviously, it is insufficient if it is anticipated that occupants may suffer disconnection of their supplies, possibly because they cannot pay, for longer than 72 hours. In practice, research has suggested that such cases lie in the long tail of the distribution of periods for which people may be disconnected. Such cases are relatively rare, but the periods of disconnection can be very long and indeterminate. Specifying a practical limit may then be difficult, and the only solution may be to rely on smoke alarms with standby batteries that are capable of operating the smoke alarms for a long period in the quiescent state and still be capable of giving an alarm signal (possibly of limited duration) in the event of fire.

In considering any standby period, it is important to ensure that, during the entire standby period, there is sufficient capacity to give an alarm (which will demand much more current than the standby situation) for long enough if fire occurs. Thus, the Code recommends that, at the end of the 72 hours, there should be sufficient capacity to supply the maximum alarm load for a specified period of time. In the case of Grades A–C systems, the maximum alarm load will involve all alarm sounders operating and all detectors in the alarm condition (unless the system somehow restricts the number of detectors that can initiate alarm signals simultaneously).

The minimum period for which the systems should be capable of giving an alarm at the end of the 72 hour period varies according to the Grade of system. The periods recommended for each Grade are set out below, along with other recommendations specific to each Grade of system.

Grade A systems

By definition, the power supplies for these systems should comply with the recommendations of BS 5839-1: 2002, except those in sub-clause 25.4 e), which deals with the standby duration.

Compliance with BS 5839-1 necessitates a dedicated circuit for the mains supply to the fire alarm system, segregated, in accordance with the recommendations of BS 5839-1, from other electrical circuits.

The fire alarm circuit should have its own circuit breaker or similar device close to the origin of the supply to the dwelling. This should be labelled to indicate its function and to warn that it should not be switched off. In addition, close to the control panel (or any separate power supply unit in which there is mains voltage), there should be a suitable means for double pole isolation of the mains supply to facilitate local isolation during maintenance. Any device that isolates the mains supply should be suitably labelled.

BS 5839-1 recommends against protection of supplies from which the fire detection system is derived by any residual current device (rcd). Such devices can be subject to nuisance tripping, so reducing the reliability of the normal supply to the fire detection system. However, rcd protection may be necessary for reasons of electrical safety. In this case, BS 5839-1 recommends that any fault on a general electrical circuit in the building should not cause the supply to the fire detection system to be isolated.

With regard to the duration of the standby batteries, after the 72 hour standby period (during which there will be additional current drawn by the visual and audible indication of mains failure given by the control and indicating equipment), BS 5839-6 recommends that there should be sufficient power to give a general alarm (in response to a fire that results in operation of all fire detectors in the dwelling) for 15 minutes.

Unlike BS 5839-1, the Code recommends against reducing the standby battery capacity if there is an automatically started standby generator. A generator would, of course, not be found in many dwellings other than, perhaps, very large country mansions. The maintenance of any such generator may not be of the same standard as those in industrial and commercial premises. Reliance on them for operation of the fire detection system would probably be unwise. Moreover, the presence of a standby generator is irrelevant in the event of failure of the individual mains circuit that supplies the fire detection system.

On the other hand, there are some mansions and stately homes that are, for security reasons alone, quite literally never left unattended. The staff present may well be able to arrange for rectification of faults in the supply to the fire detection system. In such circumstances, the Code permits the 72 hour standby period to be reduced to 24 hours.

Grade B systems

The mains supply for a Grade B system will be similar in nature to the supply for a Grade A system. The Code recommends that the mains supply be dedicated to the fire alarm system and that the fuse or circuit breaker serving the circuit be suitably labelled to warn against isolation of the supply. The circuit should not be protected by an rcd, unless this is necessary for reasons of electrical safety. In the latter case, the Code offers two alternatives, in order to avoid faults on other circuits causing failure of the supply to the fire detection system. Either any rcd that could result in isolation of the supply to the fire detection and alarm system should be dedicated to the system, or the rcd protecting the fire alarm system circuit should operate independently of any rcd protection for circuits supplying socket outlets or portable equipment. The latter of the two options could, for example, comprise a 'split distribution board', with a time-delayed 100 mA rcd serving the entire electrical installation, including the fire detection and alarm system, while a 30 mA rcd serves all circuits supplying socket outlets or portable equipment. Thus, if a fault in an appliance results in the tripping of a rcd, it is likely that the above discrimination will ensure that it is the 30 mA rcd that trips, rather than the 100 mA rcd.

A Grade B system should have a standby battery supply that is capable of supplying the maximum alarm load for 15 minutes after the standby duration of 72 hours. The system's battery charger should be capable of recharging the batteries from their final voltage within 24 hours. The batteries used should have an expected life of, or at least, four years.

To ensure reliability of the mains supply, the Code recommends that the mains supply should be such that it can only be isolated by deliberate action on the part of the user (or, of course, in the event of a fault). This recommendation was included in the Code to ensure that the supply is not connected, for example, via a card-operated meter.

Grade C systems

Power supplies for Grade C systems should be exactly the same as those for Grade B systems with two exceptions. The first and more trivial of these is that, in the case of a system in which fire detection is integrated with another system, any warning labels should reflect this. For example, the warning label at the main electrical switch might read: 'FIRE/INTRUDER ALARM: DO NOT ISOLATE'.

Because there is a limit on the size of house that should be protected by a Grade C system, the Code recommends that, after the standby period of 72 hours, the system should be capable of supporting the maximum alarm load for only four minutes. This is consistent with the standby duration recommended for smoke alarms, and a Grade C system can, of course, simply be a number of smoke alarms connected to a central control/power supply unit.

During the 72 hour standby period, allowance should be made, when calculating the required battery capacity, for any power required to operate audible or visual warnings that arise from failure of the mains supply. The visual warning may take the form of the extinguishment of a 'mains on' indicator lamp, in which case there are no implications for the capacity of the standby batteries. However, indication could be given by illumination of a fault indicator lamp. In this case, the Code recommends that the standby batteries should be capable of operating the indicator for a total of 15 days following mains failure.

The purpose of this is to provide a facility whereby, if the normal supply has failed soon after the occupants leave for a two-week holiday, there is an indication of the failure when they return (by which time it will not be possible to rely on the standby batteries for providing a warning in the event of fire). The fire detection system need only otherwise operate correctly, of course, for the first 72 hours of the 15 day period, but it is possible that the battery capacity required to operate the fault warning indicator for the further 12 day period could be greater than that required to give an alarm for 4 minutes at the end of the 72 hour standby period.

The Code recommends that the battery capacity be governed by either the four minute alarm duration or the additional 12 day visual indication of mains failure, whichever is the greater.

During the 72 hour standby period, there will also be an audible warning when the standby battery capacity begins to fall (see the later chapter). Account should also be taken of this load when calculating standby battery capacities.

As discussed earlier in this Guide, an important form of Grade C system is one in which fire detection is integrated with an intruder alarm system. (Integration alone does not limit the grade to Grade C, but usually such integrated systems would not, for example, have the facilities necessary to satisfy the recommendations for a Grade B system.) Compliance with the British Standards relevant to intruder alarm systems does not necessitate a standby battery capacity that is sufficient to operate the system for 72 hours. Intruder detectors are likely to draw significantly more current than fire detectors. A standby period of 72 hours for the intruder alarm system may, therefore, prove to be impracticable. There are ways round this problem, such as using separate standby supplies for the intruder part of the system and the fire detection part, although, in engineering terms, this is not a particularly elegant solution. It would also be possible for the system to isolate the intruder detectors automatically after the eight hour duration, so that sufficient capacity is left to operate the fire detection system alone for the further period of 64 hours. This situation is unlikely to be received favourably by the intruder alarm industry.

However, until the industry addresses the recommendations of the Code, existing practices, whereby the standby batteries may not be capable of operating the integrated system for much more than eight hours, are likely to pertain. Nevertheless, such a system could be regarded as a Grade C system, with a variation (which would be recorded on the installation certificate) in respect of standby supply duration. The Code suggests that such a variation might be considered if the intruder alarm system has a facility for transmission of mains failure to an alarm receiving centre. Alternatively, the Code notes that it might be appropriate to regard the system as a Grade E system, in which there is normally no standby supply whatsoever. Such systems would, of course, be acceptable for retrofitting into certain existing dwellings.

Grade D systems

Because these systems incorporate a standby supply, the Code recommends that they may either be connected on a dedicated circuit supplied from the dwelling's main distribution board, or be connected to a separately electrically protected, regularly used local lighting circuit. There has been much debate about whether smoke alarms should be connected to a dedicated circuit or to a lighting circuit. Arguments in favour of the former are based on recognized good electrical engineering practices, whereby different systems are connected to different circuits, and the need to ensure the reliability of the fire detection system. With regard to the reliability issue, it is not at all unknown for a miniature circuit breaker on a lighting circuit to trip when a lamp burns out. Clearly, it would be unacceptable if this were to totally isolate the fire detection in the dwelling. Arguments in favour of connecting smoke alarms to a lighting circuit are mainly related to ensuring that the occupants do not isolate the electrical supply to their system. By connecting the smoke alarms to a regularly used lighting circuit, it can be ensured that occupants will always be aware if the mains supply to the system has failed, but will be forced to avoid intentional isolation of the supply for any length of time.

Arguably, the main disadvantage of connecting a mains-only smoke alarm (or heat alarm) to a lighting circuit is the lack of reliability of such an arrangement, particularly in the event of fire. The minimum level of coverage by smoke alarms installed in existing dwellings involves the provision of these devices in circulation areas only. General fire safety guidance to householders is that they should close all doors at night. In the event of a fire in any room in the house, it would be a brave person who would assert that a smoke alarm in the hallway would detect the fire before it caused failure of the lighting circuit, particularly if the light in the room were switched on.

In the case of smoke alarms and heat alarms with a standby supply, which the Code recommends should be of 72 hours duration, such concerns in respect of reliability, when the smoke alarms are connected to a lighting circuit, disappear. Accordingly, in the case of Grade D systems, the Code accepts either arrangement. However, as discussed in chapter 11, if smoke alarms are connected to a lighting circuit, the Code recommends that it should be possible to isolate power to the smoke alarms without isolating power to any lighting circuit; this is necessary in order to isolate a faulty smoke alarm that is permanently in the alarm condition.

In clause 22, which is a very short clause dealing with electromagnetic compatibility, there is a further comment regarding connection of smoke alarms to lighting circuits. The clause advises that, if the lighting circuit also serves fluorescent luminaires, it should be confirmed, at least by reference to the written instructions provided by the manufacturer of the smoke alarms, that the smoke alarms will not be affected when the luminaires are switched on or off. In this connection, cases have been known where the act of switching fluorescent fittings has caused, for example, a temporary bleeping of smoke alarms connected to the same circuit, which, if nothing else, would be a source of irritation to the householder. Some manufacturers' instructions warn against the practice. Often fluorescent fittings are provided in kitchens, in which case it may sometimes be preferable to connect smoke alarms on, say, the upstairs lighting circuit, rather than the one downstairs which would normally serve the kitchen.

Whichever circuit arrangement is used, the Code recommends that all interconnected smoke alarms in the dwelling are connected to the same final circuit. The reason for this is that, although the signalling voltage between smoke alarms is usually only a few volts, in the event of a fault this could obviously rise to mains voltage. Unless all smoke alarms are connected on the same circuit, a situation could arise whereby a householder working on one smoke alarm disconnects only the circuit supplying that smoke alarm, but not circuits supplying other smoke alarms. In the event of an alarm condition, a fault in one smoke alarm could cause mains voltage to appear via the interlink wire within the isolated smoke alarm. (These considerations do not apply if, as is possible, the interconnection is by radio communication, rather than by wiring.)

The capacity of the standby supply should be sufficient to power the smoke alarms or heat alarms in standby mode for 72 hours, after which there should remain sufficient capacity to give an alarm condition for four minutes. BS 5446-1 requires that the standby supply is monitored, so that an audible warning is given if its capacity fails below that required to provide the standby duration of 72 hours plus four minutes alarm load. The audible warning should normally continue for at least 24 hours after the capacity of the standby supply becomes inadequate.

Grade E systems

In the case of Grade E systems, the smoke alarms should be connected to a single independent circuit at the main distribution board. No other electrical equipment should be connected to this circuit; because there is no standby supply, the reliability of the mains supply to the smoke alarms should be as high as possible. However, a separate mains monitoring unit may be used to give warning of a failure of the supply to the smoke alarms. Obviously this device must be connected to the smoke alarm circuit. In practice, separate mains monitoring is not necessary, since BS 5446-1 requires a green 'power on' indicator to be incorporated in mains-operated smoke alarms.

We have already seen that, in the case of Grade A and Grade B systems, the Code recommends against rcd protection. No such recommendation is made in respect of Grade C or Grade D systems, presumably because of their standby supply. However, in the case of Grade E systems, the Code again recommends that the circuit serving the smoke alarms should preferably not be protected by a rcd. As discussed for a Grade B system, the Code does, however, accept that rcd protection may be necessary in order to achieve electrical safety. In this case, the Code recommends that there should either be an rcd dedicated to the smoke alarm circuit or that the rcd protection of the fire alarm circuit should operate independently of rcd protection on circuits supplying socket outlets or portable equipment.

As in the case of Grade D systems, if smoke alarms (and heat alarms) can be interconnected, all smoke alarms and heat alarms should be connected on a single final circuit, unless the interconnection is by means of radio communication.

Grade F systems

The batteries in the smoke alarms and heat alarms of a Grade F system should be capable of operating the smoke and heat alarms for at least one year, assuming that the devices are tested every week. It is doubtful whether most householders do actually test their smoke alarms every week, but this is recommended in the Code (see chapter 25).

Battery fault monitoring is required by BS 5446-1, so that an audible fault warning is given whenever the battery capacity drops below a minimum acceptable level. In order to define this level, the Code recommends that, as is required by BS 5446-1, when the battery fault warning commences, the batteries should either be able to give a fire alarm signal for at least four minutes or to continue the battery fault warning for at least 30 days, whichever is the greater. Although the fault warning should continue for at least 30 days, it is not necessary for the detector to be capable of operating correctly and giving an alarm for the full 30 days. Such a recommendation would probably be unreasonable, albeit achievable, since other Grades of system need operate for only 72 hours after fault warnings.

18. Wiring

Clause 16 of the Code makes recommendations in respect of the wiring used in domestic fire detection and alarm systems. (The Code also recognizes the use of 'wire-less' systems, and recommendations in respect of these are given in clause 21.)

Because the time required to escape from most dwellings is very short compared with escape times in industrial and commercial buildings (and indeed the time between detection of fire and untenable conditions for occupants can be very short anyway), in most situations the cables used need not have any specific fire resistance. However, care should be taken to ensure that wiring is not susceptible to damage, particularly if the cables are unmonitored and damage to them could remain undetected for some time. In the case of systems employing smoke alarms, the design of the smoke alarm circuits should be such that any fault on the interconnecting wiring should not prevent the individual smoke alarms from functioning correctly.

The particular recommendations in respect of wiring vary according to the Grade of system. The recommendations of the Code in respect of each Grade are considered below.

Grade A systems

Since these systems are generally designed in accordance with the recommendations of BS 5839-1, the Code recommends that wiring should comply with the recommendations of sub-clause 26.2 of that standard for, at least, cables of standard fire resistance. The most significant implication of this recommendation is that all cables used in the installation, including those carrying the mains supply to control equipment, should be fire resisting.

In recent years, there has been much controversy regarding the performance required from fire alarm cables during the course of a fire.

The 1988 version of BS 5839-1 divided fire alarm circuits into two groups, namely those required to operate for a prolonged period during the course of a fire and those not required to do so. No fire performance requirements were recommended for the latter group of cables. However, the 1988 version of BS 5839-1 recommended that the former cables should either comprise mineral insulated copper sheathed cable or cables capable of achieving a certain performance if tested in accordance with BS 6387[10], but other types of cable could also be used provided they were suitably protected against fire by burial in the structure of the building or separation from any significant fire risk by structural fire protection. It was to the recommendations of BS 5839-1: 1988 that the 1995 version of BS 5839-6 referred in respect of cables used in Grade A systems.

The controversy that has raged in recent years concerns the manner in which cables are tested in accordance with BS 6387. The tests specified in BS 6387 include one to verify resistance to fire alone. There is then a further test to verify resistance to fire in conjunction with water spray (reflecting the fact that, during a fire, water will be discharged onto the fire from extinguishers, hose reels and/or sprinkler heads), and a third test to verify the resistance of the cable to fire in conjunction with mechanical shock (reflecting the fact that, during a fire, objects may fall).

The controversy has centred around the matter of whether all three tests should be carried out on a single sample of cable or whether, as actually happens, a separate sample is used for each of the three tests. Particularly, it has been claimed that, generally, mineral insulated copper sheathed cables can pass all three tests even if they are carried out on a single sample of cable, whereas it is claimed that this is not generally true of soft-skinned cables.

This controversy has been resolved in the 2002 version of BS 5839-1, which also, to some extent, simplifies the recommendations in respect of the fire resistance of cables. Firstly, BS 5839-1 now recommends that all cable systems used for all parts of the critical signal paths, and for the low voltage mains supply to the system, should be fire resisting. It should be noted that this recommendation applies to the cable itself; protection of a non-fire resisting cable by building construction will not satisfy the recommendations. It should also be noted that this recommendation applies to the entire length of mains supply cable to the system, from the point at which the circuit is first dedicated to the fire alarm system.

However, BS 5839-1 now divides fire resisting cables into two types, according to their level of fire resistance, namely 'standard fire resisting

---

[10] BS 6387: 1994. *Specification for performance requirements for cables required to maintain circuit integrity under fire conditions.*

cables' and 'enhanced fire resisting cables'. BS 5839-1 specifies performance levels for each of the two groups of cables. Rather than these performance levels relating to BS 6387, the tests relate to EN 50200[11] in conjunction with additional performance recommendations specified in BS 5839-1. The performance levels themselves were developed largely by determining the level of performance that can, in the case of enhanced fire resistance, reasonably be expected in the case of a mineral insulated copper sheathed cable, and that can, in the case of standard fire resistance, reasonably be expected of any of the existing proprietary fire resisting cables that have been certificated as conforming to BS 7629.

In response to BS 5839-1: 2002, the cable industry have launched a new generation of 'soft-skinned' cables, which satisfy the recommendations for enhanced fire resistance. As BS 5839-1 is a code of practice, rather than a product standard, it is inappropriate, in the long term, for that standard to contain specifications for products. Two new test standards, based on the recommendations within BS 5839-1, have been developed and published as BS 8434 Parts 1 and 2. In the future, therefore, it is quite likely that BS 5839-1 will be amended to remove performance recommendations for cables, which could then be replaced by a simple reference to performance in the the relevant part of BS 8434.

BS 5839-1 acknowledges that cables capable of complying with the recommendations for standard fire resistance include some that have been commonly used for many years for circuits in fire alarm systems that must operate for a prolonged period during a fire, without any evidence from real fires that satisfaction of the objectives of the fire alarm system necessitates a higher performance. However, BS 5839-1 recognizes that the level of fire resistance described as 'enhanced' is desirable in certain situations. Four such situations are described in BS 5839-1, and none of these are likely to apply to dwellings. They comprise unsprinklered buildings in which the fire strategy involves evacuation of occupants in four or more phases, unsprinklered buildings of greater than 30 m in height, unsprinklered premises in which it is envisaged people will remain in occupation during the course of a fire, and any other buildings in which the designer, specifier or regulatory authority, on the basis of a fire risk assessment that takes fire engineering considerations into account, considers that the use of enhanced fire resisting cables is necessary.

It is unlikely that even a large HMO would exceed 30 m in height, although if a large block of flats were treated as an HMO of the type to which BS 5839-6 applies, and a single fire alarm system were necessary

---

[11] EN 50200. *Method of test for resistance to fire of unprotected small cables for use in emergency circuits.*

throughout the block, then all the cables would need to be those of enhanced fire resistance. In theory, if the fire precautions in a dwelling were designed as a 'fire engineering solution', as opposed to following prescriptive codes in respect of means of escape, etc., it would be open to an enforcing authority to demand cables of enhanced fire resistance for an automatic fire detection system that formed an integral part of the solution. In practice, it is very difficult to envisage circumstances in which this would be a reasonable demand.

To ensure mechanical strength, BS 5839-1 recommends that, whatever cable is used, all conductors should have a cross-sectional area of at least 1 mm^2. To avoid the risk of mechanical damage to the cables, they should not be installed within the same conduit as the cables of other services. Where the cables share common trunking with other cables, a separate compartment of the trunking, separated from other compartments by a strong, rigid and continuous partition, should be reserved solely for fire alarm cables. The purpose of this recommendation is to avoid damage to the fire alarm cables when modifications are carried out to other circuits (e.g. other cables are stripped out). When a new fire alarm system is retrofitted to a building, it would, of course, be possible to consider a variation from this recommendation for economy of installation, particularly in the case of mains supply cables for the fire alarm system; care might, however, be required in the case of other circuits in order to avoid any chance of electromagnetic interference to fire alarm circuits from circuits of other services.

Mineral insulated copper sheathed cables and steel wire armoured cables may be used throughout all parts of a BS 5839-1 system without additional mechanical protection, except in particularly arduous conditions. BS 5839-1 recommends that other cables should be given mechanical protection in any areas in which physical damage or rodent attack is likely. More specifically, other than in relatively benign environments in which cable is clipped directly to robust construction, mechanical protection should be provided for these other cables in all areas that are less than 2 m above floor level. The term 'relatively benign environments' is not specifically defined, but, since the main concern relates to mechanical damage, a dwelling can be considered a benign environment; consideration of additional protection (e.g. use of trunking) might, however, be necessary if there is a risk of rodent attack.

To further ensure the integrity of the fire alarm circuits, BS 5839-1 recommends that cables should be installed without external joints wherever practicable. Where jointing of cables is necessary, other than in the case of joints within components of the system, the terminals used to joint the cables should be constructed of materials that will withstand a similar temperature and duration of temperature to that of the cable itself.

This recommendation is likely to preclude the use of certain plastic terminal blocks. The joints should be enclosed within junction boxes, labelled with the words 'FIRE ALARM', to assist in the identification of fire alarm circuits.

In the same way that any joints in cables should not compromise the fire resistance of the overall cable system, methods of cable support should be such that circuit integrity is not reduced. The methods of support should withstand a similar temperature, and duration of temperature, to the cable itself, while maintaining adequate support. As pointed out in BS 5839-1, this recommendation, in effect, precludes the use of plastic cable clips, cable ties or trunking, where these products are the sole means of cable support.

Finally, there remains the matter of protecting fire alarm cables from any detrimental influence of other circuits. BS 5839-1 recommends, therefore, that, where multi-core cable is used for interconnection of fire alarm circuits, none of the conductors should be used for circuits other than those of the fire alarm system. To avoid electromagnetic interference with the fire alarm signals, care needs to be taken that any recommendations by the manufacturer of the fire alarm equipment in respect of separation of fire alarm cables from the cables of other services are followed.

Furthermore, fire alarm cables carrying power in excess of extra-low voltage (e.g. at 230 V) should be segregated from extra-low voltage fire alarm circuits (e.g. 24 V circuits). However, BS 5839-1 recognizes the types of cable specified within clause 26 of BS 5839-1 as, themselves, a suitable form of segregation, subject to compliance with any recommendations by the manufacturer of the fire alarm equipment in respect of separation for the purposes of avoiding electromagnetic interference. Nevertheless, BS 5839-1 recommends that the mains supply to any control, indicating or power supply equipment should not enter the equipment through the same cable entry as cables carrying extra-low voltage. Within the equipment itself, low voltage and extra-low voltage cables should be kept separate to the extent practicable.

Having segregated the fire alarm circuits from other circuits and, in the case of trunking, kept the fire alarm cables within a separate compartment from other circuits, it is important that this situation is maintained. It is also important that there is no interference with fire alarm circuits as a result of confusion between these circuits and other circuits. Accordingly, BS 5839-1 recommends that all fire alarm cables should be of a single, common colour that is not used for cables of general electrical services in the building. While a note in clause 26 of the BS 5839-1 states that the colour red is preferred, it would be possible to comply with the Code by using another colour, provided the same colour is not used for cables of other electrical services in the building.

Grade B systems

The recommendations in respect of wiring for Grade B systems are virtually identical to those for Grade A systems. The only relaxations that apply in the case of Grade B systems are that the cables need not be colour-coded to distinguish them from other circuits, nor need cables be installed in separate conduits, or a separate compartment within trunking, from other cables, unless this is necessary to avoid electromagnetic interference.

As in the case of Grade A systems, the wiring to alarm sounders and detectors should be monitored. However, in the case of Grade B systems, a short circuit on the wiring to detectors may give rise to a fire alarm signal or a fault signal, whereas in the case of Grade A systems, only the latter would be permitted.

Grade C systems

Wiring of Grade C systems need not be capable of surviving the effects of fire for any length of time. The cables used should simply be those required to satisfy normal electrical engineering considerations.

However, if the cables are likely to be subject to damage or rodent attack, additional protection against such damage should be provided. Protection can be provided by the building construction (e.g. plaster finishes) or by conduit, ducting or trunking.

Grade D and Grade E systems

There are few recommendations that apply to the wiring of smoke alarms; the cable used can simply be any cable suitable for domestic mains voltage wiring, and it should be installed in accordance with IEE Regulations (BS 7671).

Otherwise, the Code simply recommends that the cores used for transmission of power be easily distinguishable (normally by colour) from those used for signalling between interconnected smoke alarms. It is also recommended that, because the wiring is unmonitored, in any areas where the cable may be subject to impact, abrasion or rodent attack, it should be provided with mechanical protection in the same manner as described for mechanical protection in a Grade C system.

Grade F systems

For interconnection of battery-operated smoke alarms, any cables suitable for the voltage and current concerned may be used. The Code recommends that the cable should be protected against damage (as described for Grades C, D and E systems) in areas where it may be subject to impact, abrasion or rodent attack.

19. Control and indicating equipment

Only Grades A, B and C systems incorporate any form of control and indicating equipment. Such systems are not normally necessary for protection of life in a normal-sized single-family dwelling.

However, where control and indicating equipment is provided, as in the case of larger dwellings, consideration should be given to its siting. In systems of the type described in BS 5839-1, an important function of the equipment is to provide an indication to those responding to an alarm signal, particularly the fire service, as to the location of a fire. When the fire alarm system operates in a very large dwelling, occupiers are likely to go to the control equipment to find out the source of the alarm signal. For these reasons, the Code recommends that control and indicating equipment should be sited on the same level as the normal entrance to the dwelling, close to the normal entrance. If, then, there is a fire, occupants can escape quickly, even if their first action was to go to the control and indicating equipment.

In single-family dwellings, dwellings with long-term lodgers and houses shared by no more than six persons who live in much the same way as a single family (e.g. student houses), occupants are likely to know where the fire alarm control panel is located. Accordingly, the Code permits it to be hidden from view. In contrast, in HMOs, the equipment should be sited in a common circulation area, close to the door by which the fire service enter the property.

Whatever control equipment is provided, the mounting height should be such that all controls are at least 1.5 m above floor level to prevent tampering by the little fingers of the junior members of the household. However, if the occupants are wheelchair bound, the mounting height may be lower.

The control and indicating equipment used in Grade A systems should, by definition, conform to the requirements of BS EN 54-2. Such equipment is designed to the high standards required for protection of onerous industrial occupancies. The equipment must be capable of passing numerous environmental tests, including dry heat, damp heat, cold, vibration, electrostatic discharge, electromagnetic interference, etc. The product standard also makes very detailed and specific requirements in respect of the facilities provided and the functional performance of the equipment.

However, BS EN 54-2 does not require the provision of zonal indicators; for example, a text display could be used to give the location of the fire. This would not, however, be acceptable under BS 5839-6 (or BS 5839-1), both of which recommend that, in multi-zone systems, there be separate light-emitting indicators for each zone. This is to assist the fire service, by providing an 'at a glance' indication of the fire location and spread of fire.

BS EN 54-2 control equipment may also be used in a Grade B system (without zonal indicators). (Use of this equipment will not necessarily, by itself, convert the Grade from B to A, as there are other relaxations applicable to Grade B systems.) However, in many dwellings, there is less need for such expensive, complex and robust control and indicating equipment. For this reason, the Code describes, in Annex C, a much simpler control panel, which it is considered would be suitable for Grade B systems. In effect, the Annex is like a small product standard within the code of practice.

The intent of this Annex is to provide an opportunity for the industry to offer a relatively cheap and simple product that would permit an affordable fire detection and alarm 'system' (in the more usual sense of the word), over which the user would have much better control and that would have a greater degree of monitoring, than a 'system' comprising smoke alarms. Unfortunately, manufacturers have not developed products to meet this Annex, which appeared in the 1995 version of the Code. Nevertheless, the Annex remains within the Code to permit the use of a very simple control panel for Grade B systems.

The Grade B control panel is basically one that need comprise nothing more complicated than two switches, three lamps and an internal sounder. The functions of these are as follows:

- A red lamp to indicate visually a fire alarm signal.
- A green lamp to indicate that the mains supply is healthy.
- An amber lamp to indicate a fault condition.
- A silence control to silence sounders. (Unlike the silence control in a BS EN 54-2 panel, this may simply be a switch that isolates the alarm sounders, but in this case a further switch will be required to silence the audible fault warning.)

- A reset control to enable the system to be reset after an alarm condition. (This may actually be an isolate control in the detector circuit.)
- An internal sounder to indicate fire or fault conditions.

Note that the same internal sounder may be used to indicate a fire condition and a fault condition. Discrimination is not too important because it will not be this sounder on which people depend to be given a warning of fire; there will be alarm sounders in the dwelling.

Grade C control and indicating equipment can be very simple indeed. The main features are that the equipment should be capable of supplying power from a main and standby source to the detectors, which may be smoke alarms, and to any separate sounders (if smoke alarms are not used), and should have a means of silencing alarm conditions. The silence facility may, however, be simply a disablement control that isolates the detectors or sounders from the power supply.

There should also be a facility to indicate, by visual means, the failure of the mains supply. This may take the form of the extinguishment of a 'mains healthy' indicator or illumination of a fault lamp. However, in the latter case, the standby battery capacity should be sufficient to keep the indicator illuminated for 15 days. An audible indication should also be given when the standby batteries fail to satisfy the minimum capacity recommended in the Code.

Since dwellings protected by Grade C systems need not be sub-divided into zones, Grade C control panels need not have any form of zonal indicating equipment. However, wiring needs to be monitored so that an audible and visual fault indication is given in the event of an open or short circuit fault on wiring to detectors and sounders, unless the fault causes a fire signal to be given. (The latter may sometimes be the case in an integrated fire/ intruder alarm system.)

If additional indicators are provided they should be clearly labelled to identify their function. A failure of any visual indicator should not prevent the correct operation of any alarm sounder circuit.

20. Zoning and identification of source of alarm signals

Most dwellings, even if protected by systems incorporating control equipment, do not need to be sub-divided into zones in order for the seat of a fire to be located quickly and easily. This is made clear in clause 19 of the Code. If an addressable system is used, sub-division into zones may be even less essential, unless the dwelling is so large that the simple, crude form of indication provided by zonal indicators is of assistance to the fire brigade.

The situation is, however, quite different in the case of most of those HMOs that are within the scope of the Code. Since these are sub-divided into self-contained units, such as flats, maisonettes or bedsits, even on a relatively small floor containing several such units determination of the unit in which a detector has operated may be very time consuming if there is no one at home within them. If the HMO is large enough to warrant a Grade A system for protection of communal areas, as opposed to simply smoke alarms (to which clause 19 does not apply), the Code considers it important that anyone responding to an alarm signal should be readily able to identify the unit of accommodation from which the alarm signal has originated.

If each unit is a flat with several rooms, it may be quite reasonable to allocate a zone to each unit. However, the Code accepts that other methods of achieving the same objective may be adopted. For example, an addressable system may be used. Thus, a zone may be allocated to the floor in question, but the identification of the individual unit may take the form of a clear text display of the flat number.

More traditional means, such as remote indicator lamps outside the door of each unit, may also be used. This would be particularly easy in the case of a mixed system (see the earlier chapter), as the heat detectors on the Grade A system need only be sited just within the front door of the unit, from where the additional connection to the remote indicator will be quite short.

In the case of Grade A systems, whether installed in an HMO or a single-family dwelling, zoning should, by definition, comply with BS 5839-1. In the case of most Grade B systems, no zoning is specifically recommended by the Code. Only in the case of a two-storey dwelling exceeding 200 m² in area on either floor is zoning considered to be necessary; each floor should, in this case, be treated as a zone. (A higher dwelling of the same floor area would be outside the range of dwellings for which Grade B systems are recommended.) Grade C systems do not need to be zoned at all, although there would be no harm in the use of zonal indicators if the designer wished to provide these.

21. Manual call points

In most single-family dwellings, life safety will be sufficiently enhanced by the installation of a system that incorporates automatic detectors; there will normally be no need for the provision of manual call points. In practice, if there is a need to raise the alarm by non-automatic means, it will be sufficient to shout 'Fire'.

However, in very large houses, and in HMOs exceeding the size for which smoke alarms are sufficient (i.e. more than two storeys or more than 200 m² on any storey), manual call points should be installed. This recommendation in clause 18 of the Code applies to both Category PD and Category LD systems. Manual call points are of value for both life safety and property protection because, if people are present in an area where a fire starts, they will detect the fire before an automatic detector. If they then operate a manual call point, people will be given the earliest possible warning, so contributing to their safety, while, for property protection, the automatic transmission of the fire signal to an alarm receiving centre will ensure that the fire service is quickly summoned.

For very large single-family dwellings (including those with long-term lodgers) and very large dwellings shared by no more than six persons, a pragmatic approach is adopted in the Code. Manual call points are recommended if a verbal warning of fire, shouted by a person on the ground floor, is unlikely to be heard by all occupants. A note to the Code makes it clear, however, that this recommendation is not intended to cater for the loud stereo of a teenager in a typical single-family dwelling! The note suggests that the solution is only likely to apply to houses with four or more storeys above ground level and large multi-storey mansions, country houses, etc. Nevertheless, the note also suggests that the provision of manual call points should at least be considered in any Grade A system.

In the case of HMOs, manual call points should always be provided, except in single-family dwellings with long-term lodgers, houses shared by no more than six persons, and HMOs of only one or two storeys with no floor greater than 200 m^2 in area (for which smoke alarms would be acceptable). Of course, in the first two cases, manual call points could be necessary as a result of the size of the property, using the criteria described above.

Where manual call points are provided, the Code recommends that they should conform to the requirements of BS EN 54-11 for type A manual call points. This is the conventional British manual call point, which triggers the alarm when the glass is broken or displaced (as opposed to type B manual call points, in which two actions, such as breaking a glass and pushing a button, are required to trigger the alarm). Although not specifically stated in the Code, subject to the agreement of the enforcing authority, in an HMO in which there is constant malicious operation of manual call points, the use of manual call points with hinged, transparent covers would seem a reasonable variation; this is recognized in BS 5839-1 in any case.

The delay between operation of a manual call point and the sounding of the alarm signal should not exceed three seconds. This is an important point to highlight, since BS EN 54-2 permits the delay to be as long as ten seconds. However, such a long delay could cause confusion of occupants, who might consider that the system has failed to operate and then begin to seek another manual call point, or take other inappropriate action, so putting themselves at greater risk. Accordingly, the recommendations of the Code are more stringent than those in the standard for control equipment. In this respect, therefore, the use of a BS EN 54-2 control panel would not guarantee compliance with the Code.

The recommendations of the Code in respect of siting call points are almost identical to those in BS 5839-1. Call points should be sited on escape routes (i.e. in an HMO, in the common parts and not the dwelling units), at each storey exit, all principal exits to open air, and, additionally, so distributed that no one need travel further than 45 m to reach the nearest call point. The reference to 'principal' exits is intended to preclude the need for call points to be sited at every door that leads directly from a room to open air (e.g. French doors from a living room to a garden). However, a 'back door' would be treated as a principal exit. At storey exits, call points can be sited close to the door to a protected staircase or on the staircase landing.

Normally, the call points should be sited at a height of 1.2 m above the finished floor level. This is lower than the figure of 1.4 m recommended in BS 5839-1 (albeit that the latter code does accept a 'tolerance' of 200 mm). The lower figure is to cater more readily for disabled people in wheelchairs.

Manual call points can generally be flush mounted, even in long corridors of single-family dwellings, as occupants will be aware of their locations. However, in an HMO, the Code recommends that, in corridors, the manual call points should not be flush mounted. So that they are readily visible if approached from the side, their front face should stand proud of the wall by at least 15 mm.

22. Remote transmission of alarm signals

Normally, if a fire occurs in a dwelling, the fire brigade will be summoned by the 999 (or 112) public emergency call service. This is normally satisfactory as far as the life safety of the occupants is concerned. Clause 20 of the Code, which deals with remote transmission of alarm signals, almost positively discourages automatic remote transmission of fire alarm signals to the fire service from most dwellings. The reason is that the Code regards it as essential that false alarms are not unnecessarily passed to the fire service. Thus, the Code asserts that, in most dwellings, automatic transmission of fire signals to the fire service is unnecessary. The Code also points out that, such is the rate of false alarms in domestic fire alarm systems, if all such systems had remote transmission facilities the burden on fire services would be totally unacceptable.

However, as discussed in an earlier chapter, domestic fire detection is sometimes integrated with intruder alarm systems, which do commonly have facilities for transmission of signals to an alarm receiving centre. Having provided this equipment, it is then almost 'too easy' to transmit fire signals as well as intruder alarm signals, regardless of whether this is necessary for life safety; it is, of course, difficult to prevent occupiers from enjoying the benefits that undoubtedly ensue as far as property protection is concerned.

Indeed, the Code acknowledges this benefit to property protection and that, for some Category PD systems, such as those protecting large properties of high value or with high value contents, not only is remote transmission of alarms warranted, but it may be a requirement of the fire insurer. Automatic transmission can also be warranted if occupants are mobility impaired or suffer from speech impairments.

In sheltered housing, it is normal practice for the smoke alarms in dwellings to transmit fire signals to a third party, such as an on-site warden, in the same way as the social alarm system (comprising alarms from pull cords, etc.) does. This would normally be a requirement imposed under building regulations. If the warden is on-site, it may be appropriate to investigate the alarm signal and/or use a speech intercom facility to communicate with occupants, before calling the fire service. Where transmission of social alarm signals is to an off-site monitoring facility (as often occurs outside the normal working hours of an on-site warden), again it might be appropriate for the monitoring centre to attempt to establish communication with occupiers before summoning the fire service.

Notwithstanding the generally negative approach towards the provision of remote transmission facilities adopted in clause 20, much of the philosophy described above actually occurs within the commentary of clause 20, rather than the 'auditable' recommendations, which are set out in sub-clause 20.2. In any case, as discussed above, even the commentary does acknowledge the benefits of automatic transmission facilities under certain circumstances.

Where automatic transmission is considered essential, the commentary of the Code also expresses a preference for systems in which the transmission path is continuously monitored. The obvious example of such a system is British Telecom's RedCARE transmission system, in which alarm and line monitoring signals are transmitted over normal telephone lines, which can also be used for normal speech telephony without interfering with the alarm transmission function. This is in contrast with systems that use devices, such as digital communicators, which 'dial up' the alarm monitoring centre to establish a connection when transmission of a signal is required. Because there is no continuous monitoring of the communications path in such systems, the period for which the system might be disabled in the event of a fault can be significantly longer than systems such as RedCARE, albeit that RedCARE is not available in all areas of the United Kingdom. It should, however, be noted that this 'preference' for monitored systems is expressed in the commentary of clause 20, rather than the definitive recommendations of that clause. Accordingly, failure to use a monitored system would not constitute a variation from the recommendations of the Code. However, the Code does specifically recommend against the use of systems (often known as '999 auto-diallers') that transmit a pre-recorded speech message automatically to the fire service via the public emergency call system.

Turning to the recommendations themselves, notwithstanding that remote transmission of alarm signals is, or should be, the exception rather than the rule, the recommendations in respect of remote monitoring are quite extensive. Sub-clause 20.2, which contains these recommendations, is primarily concerned with ensuring that, where remote transmission facilities are provided, they are reliable in operation in the event of fire, and they are such as to minimize the extent to which fire services are summoned to false alarms. The recommendations do, however, begin with a positive approach to the provision of automatic transmission facilities, by recommending circumstances in which the provision of such facilities should be **considered**. Such situations comprise those in which the occupants are mobility impaired to a degree that would be likely to result in high risk in the event of fire, or where the occupants suffer from a disability, such as speech impairment, that would preclude communication by telephone with the fire service, or if the system is installed for property protection and there is a need for early attendance of the fire service when the dwelling is unoccupied.

In the third of these cases (property protection), the Code notes that the need for automatic transmission to the fire service should normally be determined by consultation with the fire insurer. In practice, often, in the case of very high value properties, the need arises from a requirement imposed by the fire insurer. If the insurer has an interest in the automatic transmission system, in that it was required by the insurer or has been taken into account by the insurer, perhaps in setting the insurance premium, the Code recommends that the method of transmission should be agreed with the insurer. Generally, the insurer will prefer systems with a monitored communications path and may well insist on this if fire detection is regarded as an important part of the measures to prevent a high financial loss.

The Code recommends that remote transmission facilities should be provided only in Grades A, B and C systems. The Code specifically recommends against transmission of signals from smoke alarms. This is because systems involving smoke alarms are considered less reliable, with less user control over the system, than systems incorporating control and indicating equipment.

The Code endeavours to ensure that occupiers and landlords take the issue of transmission of false alarms to the fire service extremely seriously. Thus, sub-clause 20.2 recommends that **before** any facility that results in automatic transmission of alarm signals to the fire service becomes operational, the organization monitoring the system (i.e. normally the company operating an alarm receiving centre) should obtain written confirmation from the occupier (or, in the case of an HMO, the landlord) that they have received, and read, written guidance regarding the importance of avoiding false alarms, suitable measures to avoid false alarms and the possible need for the fire service to force entry to the dwelling in the event of a false alarm when the dwelling is unoccupied. Annex D to the Code contains model guidance that satisfies this recommendation. Since, however, Annex D is informative, rather than normative, the exact wording of Annex D need not be adopted, but, equally, it would seem sensible that operators of alarm receiving centres use the wording in Annex D, since it has been formulated specifically to satisfy the relevant recommendation of the Code.

It should be noted that, for compliance with the Code, this guidance should be given to, and read by, occupiers before remote monitoring of fire alarm signals occurs. Moreover, in the case of an HMO, the Code recommends that the landlord should be responsible for ensuring, and confirming to the alarm receiving centre, that the guidance has been passed on to every occupier.

The issue of guidance to occupiers is extremely important for a number of reasons. Firstly, if occupiers have read the guidance before monitoring begins, there is less likelihood of transmission of the false alarms that might otherwise occur while the occupier first gets used to having a monitored fire alarm system. In this connection, the guidance in Annex D pulls no punches in stressing the need to avoid unnecessary summoning of the fire service. Thus, the Annex informs occupiers of the high rate of false alarms received by fire brigades and sets out the moral argument that, if the fire service are called to a false alarm at a dwelling, the appliances are not available to deal with real fires in the area; it is also pointed out that, in attending an emergency call, there is a risk to fire fighters and other road users.

A second benefit of the guidance is the practical information contained within it to assist occupiers in avoiding false alarms. Again, this guidance is intended to promote responsible actions by occupiers to avoid automatic transmission of false alarms to the fire service. The guidance is written in layman's language, which most occupiers should be able to understand with no difficulty.

In addition, the provision of guidance to occupiers before monitoring begins may permit something of a 'cooling off' period between placing an order for remote monitoring and the monitoring going 'live'. For example, domestic intruder alarm systems are often sold by 'door-to-door' salesmen, who can easily convince an occupier of the benefits of an intruder alarm system with remote monitoring, given the national concern that the public have in respect of crime. Little extra effort may be required to convince the householder that a few automatic fire detectors, along with remote monitoring of these detectors, constitutes a compelling value-added benefit. However, when, subsequently, the householder reads the guidance in Annex D of the Code, which the alarm receiving centre will be compelled to send to the occupier before monitoring begins, the occupier will be advised that, in some properties, 'the monitoring service might not be of much benefit'. The guidance also points out that the householder should not rely purely on an automatic transmission facility, and that, in the event of fire, an emergency call should always be made to the fire service.

For compliance with the Code, not only should this advice be studied by the householder before monitoring begins, but the advice should be provided in writing to the occupier (or landlord in the case of an HMO) at periods not exceeding twelve months. Thus, for example, when an annual contract for monitoring is renewed, the alarm receiving centre should, again, send out this advice.

Also, every twelve months, the organization that monitors the fire alarm system is required, for compliance with the Code, to verify that there is a contract in place for maintenance of the fire alarm system at least every six months. The Code specifically recommends against remote monitoring of alarm signals unless such a contract is in place, other than in the case of smoke alarms connected to social alarm systems. In the latter case, six-monthly maintenance is still a recommendation of the Code (see chapter 25), but the Code does not preclude remote monitoring of the system if users fail to comply with this recommendation; this reflects the greater need for remote monitoring in the case of social alarm systems.

It was noted above that the Code does define circumstances in which provision of remote monitoring should at least be considered. In all circumstances other than these, if remote monitoring is provided, effectively in circumstances beyond those recommended for consideration by the Code, a form of alarm filtering should be incorporated to avoid transmission of false alarms to the fire service. This filtering arrangement can take either one of two forms. The first is 'alarm verification', whereby, on receipt of a fire alarm signal, the alarm receiving centre endeavours to contact the dwelling by telephone to determine whether there is a real fire. If this cannot be established within two minutes from completion of the dialling process, the alarm signal should then be passed to the fire service without further delay.

Alternatively, in the second arrangement, the two minute delay could be applied by the system within the dwelling, so that the fire alarm signal is not transmitted to the alarm receiving centre until two minutes after the audible fire alarm signal is given within the dwelling. This permits the occupier to take positive action to prevent transmission of the alarm signal to the alarm receiving centre. The latter arrangement is only likely to apply to systems of greater sophistication; since these are only likely to be installed in very large properties, the Code suggests that the two minute delay period might be increased to as much as four minutes if this longer period is required by occupants to investigate the fire alarm signal and then reach the relevant control to prevent automatic transmission to the alarm receiving centre. (It should be noted that the means of preventing the alarm transmission cannot involve simply silencing of audible alarm sounders, since the Code recommends that automatic transmission of fire alarm signals should not be prevented by the act of silencing fire alarm sounders, nor should it depend on the state of any silencing switch.) This time delay, which is, effectively, the 'staff alarm' described in BS 5839-1 for non-domestic systems, could also be incorporated within a Category PD system, but the Code suggests that this should occur only if the system is considered to have a high potential for false alarms and if the time delay is agreed with the property insurers.

Grade A systems generally incorporate quite sophisticated facilities at the control and indicating equipment. Accordingly, the Code recommends that, in Grade A systems, a means should be provided for disablement of any automatic transmission facility. The intention is that this can be used when there is potential for false alarms and during periods of testing and maintenance. Since the control equipment in a Grade A system will comply with BS EN 54-2, use of any such disablement control will result in a warning at the control equipment.

It has been pointed out earlier in this chapter that, often, the equipment used for transmission of fire alarm signals to an alarm receiving centre will be the same equipment that has been provided for transmission of other alarm signals, such as intruder alarm signals or social alarm signals. Accordingly, the Code points out that, in these cases, there should be discrimination between fire alarm signals and other alarm signals. This includes signals from fire alarm systems in sheltered housing transmitted to a warden's site monitoring facility. However, sometimes, in sheltered housing, smoke alarms are retrofitted into dwelling units, and there may not be any readily available facility to transmit separate fire signals from these smoke alarms to the warden. The Code recognizes this potential situation, and the note advises that, if smoke detectors are retrofitted to an existing social alarm system (to form, in effect, a Grade C system) that has no facilities for discrimination between different types of alarm signal, the recommendation for distinguishable signals need not be followed, provided that the pre-planned response by the warden to signals from the fire detection system in any dwelling is identical to the pre-planned response to other alarm signals (such as operation of a pull cord by an occupant); this assumes, of course, that the pre-planned response is appropriate in the event of fire.

The Code recommends that any alarm receiving centre to which fire alarm signals are relayed should comply with the recommendations of BS 5979[12]. Both the Loss Prevention Certification Board and the National Security Inspectorate operate schemes for third-party certification of alarm receiving centres to BS 5979. Perhaps the most important implication of this recommendation is that the alarm receiving centre will need suitable means for effective communication with the relevant fire service control room. Unfortunately, it is not unknown for companies operating alarm receiving

---

[12] BS 5979: 2000. *Code of practice for remote centres receiving signals from security systems.*

centres to accept facilities for monitoring fire alarm systems in areas of the country for which there is no proper means for communication between the alarm receiving centre and the fire service. Cases have been known where the alarm receiving centre have endeavoured to contact the fire service on an administrative telephone number, which may not be answered, or may be subject to significant delays in answering, outside normal office hours. It is also not unknown for the alarm receiving centre to contact one fire brigade, with whom there is a proper means of communication, to pass on a call within the area of another fire service in a completely different area of the country. However, these arrangements would not comply with the recommendations of BS 5979. A particular benefit of the Loss Prevention Certification Board ('LPCB') scheme is that, in listing alarm receiving centres that are certificated under the scheme, the areas of the country with which the LPCB have confirmed there is adequate communication with the fire service are specifically listed.

The Code makes a number of recommendations to ensure reliability of automatic transmission systems. Where the alarm transmission device is in a separate enclosure from the fire alarm control and indicating equipment (which will normally be the case), the connection between the two should be monitored, so that an audible and visual fault signal is given in the event of an open or short circuit fault on the interconnecting cable. In practice, it is usually very difficult indeed to comply with this recommendation. Most fire alarm control panels do not have a monitored output that is specifically intended for this purpose. Instead, it is common to link the transmission device to the common fire relay within the fire alarm control panel. Often, the way the circuit is configured is such that an open circuit fault will result in a false alarm, while a short circuit fault will prevent a fire alarm signal at the control panel being transmitted by the transmission equipment. It would seem likely that a possible practical solution would be to combine the fire alarm system and the alarm transmission device. For example, the two enclosures could abut, so that there is, in effect, no external wiring to monitor. Alternatively, in an addressable system, an input/output unit on a detector loop could be mounted within, or could abut, the enclosure of the alarm transmission equipment.

Logically, the Code recommends that the power supplies for the automatic transmission equipment should satisfy the recommendations of the Code for power supplies for the fire detection system itself. As discussed in chapter 17, the implications of this recommendation will depend on the Grade of system that is being monitored. However, in each case, probably the most important implication relates to standby battery capacity, which will need to be sufficient to maintain the transmission equipment in the standby state for at least 72 hours, after which sufficient capacity should remain to support alarm transmission for 15 minutes in the case of Grade A and Grade B systems, or four minutes in the case of Grade C systems. If the alarm transmission equipment has primarily been provided for transmission of intruder alarm systems, the standby battery capacity is likely to fall far short of this recommendation; an increase in battery capacity would be necessary.

Care needs to be taken, in the case of Category PD systems, that a fire cannot damage the transmission equipment before it is detected and a signal transmitted to an alarm receiving centre. To address this need, the Code offers two alternatives. Either the area in which the transmission equipment is installed should be protected by automatic fire detection, or it should be installed in an area of low fire risk. Area of low fire risk is not defined in the Code, but this should probably not be interpreted as stringently as the 'area of low fire risk' described in BS 5839-1, which is effectively a sterile area. Equally, BS 5839-6 notes that an electrical distribution cupboard (in which transmission equipment is often installed) is *not* an area of low fire risk.

23. The use of radio-linked systems in dwellings

The principle of using radio, instead of wiring, to link fire detectors, manual call points and fire alarm sounders to control and indicating equipment is now well-established. BS 5839-1 provides special recommendations in respect of radio-linked systems, recognizing that the normal recommendations in respect of standby power supply and fault monitoring cannot be satisfied. However, although these particular relaxations from the recommendations of Part 1 apply to radio-linked systems, in general all other recommendations of Part 1 are applicable, and therefore it is possible to have a radio-linked fire detection and alarm system that complies with BS 5839-1. Accordingly, clause 21 of BS 5839-6 which deals with radio-linked systems, simply recommends that, in the case of Grades A, B and C systems, radio-linked systems should comply with the recommendations of BS 5839-1.

Radio-linked systems clearly have certain advantages for installation in dwellings. 'Wire-free' intruder alarm systems have been available for normal-sized dwellings for many years. Radio-linked systems have already made significant impact in the market for fire detection systems in stately homes and mansions, where the installation of wiring can cause disruption and can be aesthetically unacceptable. Given the experience of 'wire-free' intruder alarm systems, the ease of installation offered by radio-linked fire detection systems could possibly enable such systems to make some impact on smaller properties than those for which radio-linked systems are normally considered at present.

Although Part 6 highlights the major advantage of radio-linked systems for dwellings, namely the ease of installation and the avoidance of disfiguring décor, the disadvantage of the need to replace what could be a significant number of batteries in the case of a large installation is also highlighted. In any occupancy, battery replacement could be something of an inconvenience and could have cost penalties, although many users are prepared to accept this for the benefit of convenience in installation. However, we have already seen that the Code advocates quite strongly against the use of battery-operated smoke alarms in cases of high life risk, social deprivation, etc. The question therefore arises as to whether radio-linked systems, which depend on batteries for operation of call points, detectors, and usually also sounders, are suitable for all dwellings. Certainly, the commentary of clause 21 does suggest that these systems might be less suitable for applications in which occupants may not be able to replace batteries (perhaps due to their financial situation or their physical or mental disability) and for HMOs, in which there may be no one on the premises who is directly responsible for supervision of the system.

Nevertheless, note that the Code states that these systems might be less suitable for such applications, but not necessarily unsuitable. Why is this so, bearing in mind the advice against the use of battery-operated smoke alarms for most applications? We should firstly note that radio-linked systems had been installed in dwellings even before the 1995 version of BS 5839-6 was published. Since such systems can comply with BS 5839-1, it would be very difficult to object to their use in any new dwelling in which a building control authority required automatic fire detection, or in any HMO in which a local authority required automatic fire detection. In order to reverse quite categorically what has, presumably, been deemed to be acceptable in the past, there would need to be sound justification.

In this connection, it is not really relevant to consider radio-linked systems in the same light as battery-operated smoke alarms. Whereas the latter rely on a single source of supply, radio-linked systems have dual supplies, both of which are monitored. The possible use of lithium batteries, with quite long lifetimes, coupled with the dual nature of the power supply, makes it possible to provide a quite reliable system. Furthermore, whereas the humble battery-operated smoke alarm merely gives a local audible warning chirp as an indication of low battery, in a radio-linked system complying with BS 5839-1, a low battery in any device will result in a dedicated indication at the control and indicating equipment at least 30 days before failure of the battery. At seven days before failure, a system fault will be indicated. This gives substantial warning, of increasing severity, before battery failure.

However, in order to ensure that the reliability of any radio-linked system is commensurate with the fire risk in an HMO, the Code does contain two additional recommendations for radio-linked systems in HMOs. The reason for this is that, in some HMOs, false alarms are relatively frequent and there may be no one in overall charge of the system to ensure that causes of false alarms are addressed, false alarms are silenced once they are known to be false alarms, and to ensure that batteries in alarm sounders are replaced as soon as necessary.

The first recommendation is intended to ensure the reliability of radio-linked call points and detectors in HMOs. The Code recommends that, in HMOs, all batteries used as the normal supply for manual call points and detectors should be capable of operating the devices for at least five years before a low battery warning is given. Moreover, the Code recommends that, in determining the capacity and type of battery required to meet this recommendation, account should be taken of not only the quiescent load required to operate the devices in the normal mode, but also the additional loads resulting from weekly testing and from false alarms of five minutes' duration at the rate of two false alarms per detector per annum. In practice, these recommendations are likely to result in the use of lithium batteries.

It is also recognized that not only are low battery warning indications at the control and indicating equipment sometimes ignored, particularly if no one in particular is responsible for the installation, but that numerous fault warnings resulting from low batteries in devices can reduce confidence in the system and, possibly, even 'mask' other faults. Accordingly, in the case of an HMO, the Code recommends that, rather than waiting for low battery warnings to be given, the servicing organization should change batteries on a preventive maintenance basis before it is even likely that a low battery warning will be given.

The second recommendation is probably even more important, since it is intended to prevent all sounders from becoming inoperative as a result of prolonged false alarms. The Code recommends that, in HMOs, all battery-powered fire alarm sounders in a radio-linked system should silence automatically after 30 minutes, unless the premises are continuously supervised, so enabling manual silencing by occupants at any time that false alarms can occur. The sounders should, however, restart if, before the system is reset, a further fire alarm signal occurs.

These recommendations for radio-linked sounders are consistent with the recommendations of BS 5839-1, but it should be noted that, in BS 5839-6, they only apply to HMOs and not to single-family dwellings. In practice, radio-linked systems are generally provided with a timer to achieve this purpose, as most such systems are designed to satisfy the recommendations of BS 5839-1. Accordingly, albeit not specifically recommended by BS 5839-6, the 'time out' of radio-linked sounders in single-family dwellings might well be regarded as of benefit.

In the case of systems using smoke alarms, in which there is no control and indicating equipment, radio communication between the devices and a central point will not arise. However, the Code accepts that radio links may be used for intercommunication between smoke alarms, so obviating the need to interconnect these. (This arrangement obviates the need for all mains-operated smoke alarms to be connected to a single circuit.) The only qualification made on the use of radio for this application is that, in the case of Grade D and Grade F systems, the power drawn by the radio transmitters and receivers does not reduce the capacity of any battery or capacitor below that required to satisfy the standby durations recommended in the Code. There have been developments in the use of radio-interlinked smoke alarms, and so the use of these in the UK might well increase during the lifetime of BS 5839-6: 2004.

24. Installation, commissioning and certification

By definition, Grade A systems should be installed, tested, commissioned and certificated in accordance with all recommendations of BS 5839-1. The recommendations in the Code in respect of Grades B, C, D and E systems mostly reflect simple good practice in the installation of any electrical system. The Code refers to BS 7671 (IEE Wiring Regulations) for detailed guidance. A BS 5839-6 system is much more likely to be designed, installed, commissioned and then certificated by a single organization (often an electrical contractor) than would be the case for a BS 5839-1 system. However, it is essential that the responsibilities for each of these processes is defined, prior to commencement of installation work, particularly if more than one organization is involved.

Since recommendations in respect of the cable installation work reflect only recognized good practice, they need not be reiterated here. It should, however, be noted that cable penetrations should be fire-stopped where appropriate. In practice, in a dwelling, limitation of smoke spread is likely to be important for the safety of occupants, and it would be sensible to fill any penetration made in a solid barrier, whether it is deemed to be fire resisting or not. Although joints in cables should be avoided, any junction boxes should be labelled 'FIRE ALARM'.

In the case of Grade A and Grade B systems, the cables should be fire resisting and, in this case, methods of cable support and methods of jointing cables should not affect the integrity of the cable system to resist the effects of fire. This precludes the use of plastic cable clips, cable ties or trunking as the sole means of cable support in Grade A and Grade B systems. It also precludes the use of plastic terminal blocks, other than within devices, such as detectors and sounders. At the time of installation, other than in the case of Grade F systems, all cables should be subject to insulation resistance testing at 500 V. The minimum resistance between conductors recommended by the Code is 2 MΩ. (In practice, much higher figures should be found.)

The types of cable used and the installation standards may also have an effect on the immunity of the system to electromagnetic interference. This subject is briefly discussed in clause 22 of the Code. Some modern systems, particularly of the addressable type, can malfunction if exposed to electromagnetic fields produced by radio transmitters, portable telephones, etc., as well as by lightning and voltage transients. The subject of electromagnetic interference is a very complex one, and immunity of an installation will depend partly on the immunity of the equipment itself and on various installation factors. If smoke alarms are connected to lighting circuits that serve fluorescent luminaires, there will be a need to confirm that the smoke alarms will not be affected when these lights are switched on or off.

It is not envisaged that battery-operated smoke alarms in a Grade F system will normally be installed by a specialist. Installation recommendations for such systems are therefore minimal. The Code recommends that detectors should be rigidly fixed to permanent construction, and this probably rules out methods of fixing such as double-sided tape, unless it can be shown to be sufficiently reliable as a means of fixing. The need for avoidance of cable routes or installation techniques that make the cable susceptible to mechanical damage is also highlighted. In an earlier chapter it was noted that interconnecting wiring should be protected against damage in any areas where it may be subject to impact, abrasion or rodent attack. Although the inclusion of such recommendations in the Code may be questioned, since the Code is not intended for the householder, the purpose of including them is to ensure that they are included in instructions provided with the smoke alarms.

At commissioning, the system should be fully tested, including functional testing of smoke detectors (e.g. using a test aerosol) and heat detectors (by a heat source), even in the case of a Grade F system unless the Grade F system is installed by the householder or landlord (as would normally be the case in Grade F systems). In Grades A, B and C systems, labels should be fitted to batteries showing the date of installation. Other than in the case of Grade F systems, 'as fitted' drawings showing equipment locations, etc., should be issued to the user.

Once installation and commissioning are complete, a certificate of conformity with BS 5839-6, indicating the Grade and Category of system, should be issued. This is particularly important, and it should be noted that, in order to comply fully with the recommendations of the Code, an installation certificate must be issued. Conversely, no matter how well the system has been installed and how closely it complies with the recommendations of the Code, the installation cannot be deemed to comply fully with the Code unless a certificate of conformity has been issued. Such certificates may be required by enforcing authorities if the system has been required under legislation.

In the case of Grade A systems, there needs to be separate certification of design, installation, commissioning, and of acceptance by the purchaser, all as recommended in BS 5839-1. This has been the subject of confusion in respect of the 1995 version of BS 5839-6. Some enforcing authorities believed that, in the case of a Grade A system, the very simple certificate of compliance contained in BS 5839-6: 1995 was sufficient. In fact, since Grade A systems should comply with the recommendations of BS 5839-1, other than where the recommendations of that Code are *explicitly* overridden by BS 5839-6, Grade A systems should always have been certificated in accordance with the recommendations of BS 5839-1. In the 2004 version of BS 5839-6, any such confusion or ambiguity has been removed. The Code explicitly recommends that Grade A systems should be certificated in accordance with BS 5839-1.

For ease and avoidance of doubt, however, BS 5839-6 contains two separate annexes on the subject of certification. The first, Annex E, sets out model certificates for Grade A systems. Although the exact format of the certificates in the Annex need not be followed, all certificates should contain the information shown in the Annex, and use of the certificates will also ensure that the relevant recommendations of BS 5839-1 are satisfied. Annex F contains a much simpler single certificate for design, installation and commissioning of Grades B–F systems. The relevant model certificates in Annexes E and F are reproduced in figures 6 and 7 at the end of this chapter.

It has, however, been stressed in this guide that BS 5839-6 is only a code of practice, and not a standard that must be followed rigidly in its entirety. If it is considered appropriate to depart from the recommendations of the Code, perhaps because, in some particular circumstances, some of the recommendations may be considered inappropriate, this may be perfectly acceptable. Normally, it is necessary for such 'variations' to be agreed, however, with any interested parties. In the case of a new dwelling, this may mean consultation and agreement with the Building Control Officer, or, in the case of an HMO, it would possibly mean agreement with the Environmental Health Officer, who may choose to consult the fire authority before agreeing a particular variation. If the installation is installed for property protection, and the insurer has some interest in the installation (the insurer may, for example, have made the installation of the system a requirement of insurance), it would be appropriate to agree any variations with the insurer. On the other hand, if the installation is installed by the occupier purely for his or her own benefit, there may be no other interested party, and the variations may simply reflect the particular requirements of the occupier in consultation with the contractor.

The Code recognizes that variations may be appropriate, and recommends that they be recorded on the installation certificate. It may seem a form of tautology, but, by agreeing any variations with the interested parties and recording them on the installation certificate, the installation may be deemed to then comply with the Code!

Compliance with the Code does not, however, stop at installing the equipment, switching it on and walking away. The Code recommends that the occupier(s) of the dwelling should be provided with written operating instructions that the user can understand. Again, until such instructions have been handed over, the installer has not complied with the Code. Therefore, the model installation certificates included in Annexes E and F of the Code (see figures 6 and 7 at the end of this chapter) confirm that suitable instructions, complying with the recommendations of the Code, have been handed over.

Normally, the instructions should be supplied to the occupiers, as they are the people who will have to understand and use the system. However, in the case of an HMO, it may be difficult to identify any occupier with particular responsibility for the system. Accordingly, in the case of an HMO, the Code recommends that the instructions be handed over to the owner of the property.

The Code is quite detailed in respect of the information that should be incorporated in the instructions. As well as basic instructions on the use of controls and the meaning of visual or audible signals, the instructions should include information on matters such as how to avoid false alarms and what to do if they occur, action in the event of a fire alarm signal, testing, servicing and maintenance, etc. It is also necessary for the instructions to advise on matters of general upkeep, such as how often batteries should be replaced, the need to keep a clear space around detectors and call points, avoidance of contamination of detectors by paint, dust, etc.

These instructions are very important, and the Code advises, in effect, that matters that might be considered to be virtually basic fire safety advice, as opposed to advice on the use of the fire alarm system, should be included. For example, the Code recommends that the instructions should refer to the need to check the system on reoccupation after a vacation. An appropriate fire procedure should also be included. It should stress the importance of ensuring that all occupants leave the dwelling as quickly as possible and that the fire service is summoned immediately. It is also important that the instructions stress to the user the need to summon the fire service regardless of the size of the fire or whether there is a facility for transmission of alarms to an alarm receiving centre.

An electrician, hired to install a couple of mains-operated smoke alarms, may not be qualified to provide advice of the type described above. However, it should be noted that, in clause 24 of the Code (User instructions), the advice is that the supplier of the system should provide the written information. It is, therefore, essential that manufacturers of, in particular, the simpler systems described in the Code, which will not be installed by fire alarm specialists, carefully read clause 24 to ensure that the instructions they send out with the equipment, including the instructions within the packaging of smoke alarms, fully comply with the recommendations in that clause.

Annex E (informative)
Model certificates for Grade A systems

E.1 Design certificate

Certificate of design for the fire alarm system at:

Address: ....

....

I/We being the person(s) responsible (as indicated by my/our signatures below) for the design of
the fire alarm system, particulars of which are set out below, CERTIFY that the said design for
which I/we have been responsible complies to the best of my/our knowledge and belief with the
recommendations of Clauses 1 to **22** of BS 5839-6: 2004 and the recommendations of Section
2 of BS 5839-1: 2002 (as modified by the recommendations of BS 5839-6: 2004) for the Grade A
system described below, except for the variations, if any, stated in this certificate.

Name (in block letters): ....   Position: ....

Signature: ....   Date: ....

For and on behalf of: ....

Address: ....

....

....   Postcode: ....

The extent of liability of the signatory is limited to the system described below.

System Category (see BS 5839-6:2004, Clause **8**): ....

Variations from the recommendations of BS 5839-6 (including any variations from Section 2 of
BS 5839-1: 2002, other than those specifically recommended by BS 5839-6: 2004):

....

....

....

....

Extent of system covered by this certificate: ....

....

....

Brief description of areas protected (not applicable for Category LD1 or PD1 systems):

....

....

....

....

Detector coverage is designed to satisfy the recommendations of BS 5839-1:2002 for a Category
L1 or L2 system.

N/A ☐   L1 ☐   L2 ☐

Measures incorporated to limit false alarms. Account has been taken of the guidance contained in Section 3 of BS 5839-1: 2002 and, more specifically (tick as appropriate):

☐ Account has been taken of reasonably foreseeable causes of unwanted alarms, particularly in the selection and siting of detectors.

☐ An appropriate analogue system has been specified.

☐ An appropriate multi-sensor system has been specified.

☐ A time-related system has been specified. Details: ....

....

☐ Automatic transmission of fire alarm signals to the fire and rescue service is delayed by ......mins by a delay in transmission of fire alarm signals to the alarm receiving centre/a delay, pending verification, before the alarm receiving centre summon the fire and rescue service (delete as appropriate).

☐ Appropriate guidance has been provided for the user to enable limitation of false alarms.

☐ Other measures as follows: ....

....

Installation and commissioning

It is strongly recommended that installation and commissioning be undertaken in accordance with the recommendations of Sections 4 and 5 of BS 5839-1: 2002 respectively.

Soak test

☐ In accordance with the recommendations of **35.2.6** of BS 5839-1: 2002, it is recommended that, following commissioning, a soak period of .... should follow.

(Enter a period of not less than one week.)

☐ As the system incorporates no more than 50 automatic fire detectors, no soak test is necessary to satisfy the recommendations of BS 5839-1: 2002.

Verification

Verification that the system complies with BS 5839-1: 2002 should be carried out, on completion, in accordance with Clause 43 of BS 5839-1: 2002:

Yes ☐   No ☐   To be decided by the ☐
                               purchaser or user

Maintenance

It is strongly recommended that, after completion, the system is maintained in accordance with Section 6 of BS 5839-1: 2002.

This certificate may be required by an authority responsible for enforcement of fire safety legislation, such as the building control authority or housing authority. The recipient of this certificate might rely on the certificate as evidence of compliance with legislation. Liability could arise on the part of any organization or person that issues a certificate without due care in ensuring its validity.

E.2 Installation certificate

Certificate of installation for the fire alarm system at:

Address: ....

....

I/We being the person(s) responsible (as indicated by my/our signatures below) for the installation of the fire alarm system, particulars of which are set out below, CERTIFY that the said installation work for which I/we have been responsible complies to the best of my/our knowledge and belief with the specification described below and with the recommendations of Section 4 of BS 5839-1: 2002, except for the variations, if any, stated in this certificate.

Name (in block letters): ....   Position: ....

Signature: ....   Date: ....

For and on behalf of: ....

Address: ....

....

....   Postcode: ....

The extent of liability of the signatory is limited to the system described below.

Extent of installation work covered by this certificate:

....

....

....

Specification against which system was installed:

....

....

....

Variations from the specification and/or Section 4 of BS 5839-1 (see BS 5839-1: 2002, Clause **7**):

....

....

....

Wiring has been tested in accordance with the recommendations of Clause **38** of BS 5839-1: 2002. Test results have been recorded and provided to:

....

Unless supplied by others, the 'as fitted' drawings have been supplied to the person responsible for commissioning the system.

Supplied to the person responsible ☐   Supplied by others ☐
for commissioning the system

This certificate may be required by an authority responsible for enforcement of fire safety legislation, such as the building control authority or housing authority. The recipient of this certificate might rely on the certificate as evidence of compliance with legislation. Liability could arise on the part of any organization or person that issues a certificate without due care in ensuring its validity.

E.3 Commissioning certificate

Certificate of commissioning for the fire alarm system at:

Address: ....

....

I/We being the person(s) responsible (as indicated by my/our signatures below) for the commissioning of the fire alarm system, particulars of which are set out below, CERTIFY that the said work for which I/we have been responsible complies to the best of my/our knowledge and belief with the recommendations of Clause 39 of BS 5839-1: 2002, except for the variations, if any, stated in this certificate.

Name (in block letters): .... Position: ....

Signature: .... Date: ....

For and on behalf of: ....

Address: ....

....

.... Postcode: ....

The extent of liability of the signatory is limited to the systems described below.

Extent of system covered by this certificate: ....

....

....

Variations from the recommendations of Clause **39** of BS 5839-1: 2002 (see BS 5839-1: 2002, Clause **7**):

....

....

....

- [ ] All equipment operates correctly.
- [ ] Installation work is, as far as can reasonably be ascertained, of an acceptable standard.
- [ ] The entire system has been inspected and tested in accordance with the recommendations of **39.2**c) of BS 5839-1: 2002.
- [ ] The system performs as required by the specification prepared by: ....
  a copy of which I/we have been given.
- [ ] Taking into account the guidance contained in Section 3 of BS 5839-1: 2002, I/we have not identified any obvious potential for an unacceptable rate of false alarms.
- [ ] The documentation described in Clause **40** of BS 5839-1: 2002 has been provided to the user.

The following work should be completed before/after (delete as applicable) the system becomes operational:

....

....

....

The following potential causes of false alarms should be considered at the time of the next service visit:

....

....

....

Before the system becomes operational, it should be soak tested in accordance with the recommendations of **35.2.6** of BS 5839-1: 2002 for a period of: ....

(Enter a period of either one week, such period as required by the specification, or such period as recommended by the signatory to this certificate, whichever is the greatest, or delete if not applicable.)

This certificate may be required by an authority responsible for enforcement of fire safety legislation, such as the building control authority or housing authority. The recipient of this certificate might rely on the certificate as evidence of compliance with legislation. Liability could arise on the part of any organization or person that issues a certificate without due care in ensuring its validity.

Figure 6 Model certificates for Grade A systems

E.4 Acceptance certificate

Certificate of acceptance for the fire alarm system at:

Address: ....

....

I/We being the competent person(s) responsible (as indicated by my/our signatures below) for the acceptance of the fire alarm system, particulars of which are set out below, ACCEPT the system on behalf of:

Name (in block letters): .... Position: ....

Signature: .... Date: ....

For and on behalf of: ....

Address: ....

....

.... Postcode: ....

The extent of liability of the signatory is limited to the system described below.

Extent of system covered by this certificate: ....

....

....

- [ ] All installation work appears to be satisfactory.
- [ ] The system is capable of giving a fire alarm signal.
- [ ] The facility for remote transmission of alarms to an alarm receiving centre operates correctly. (Delete if not applicable.)

The following documents have been provided to the purchaser or user:

- [ ] 'As fitted' drawings.
- [ ] Operating and maintenance instructions.
- [ ] Certificates of design, installation and commissioning.
- [ ] A log book.
- [ ] Sufficient representatives of the user have been properly instructed in the use of the system, including, at least, all means of triggering fire signals, silencing and resetting the system and avoidance of false alarms.
- [ ] All relevant tests, defined in the purchasing specification, have been witnessed. (Delete if not applicable.)

The following work is required before the system can be accepted:

....

....

....

....

....

....

Annex F (informative)
Model certificate for Grades B, C, D, E and F systems

Certificate of design, installation and commissioning* of the fire detection and fire alarm system at:

Address: ....

....

....

....

It is certified that the fire detection and fire alarm system at the above address complies with the recommendations of BS 5839-6 for design, installation and commissioning of a Category ....,
Grade .... system, other than in the respect of the following variations:*

....

....

....

....

Brief description of areas protected (only applicable to Category LD2 and PD2 systems).

....

....

....

....

The entire system has been tested for satisfactory operation in accordance with the recommendations of **23.3**p) of BS 5839-6: 2004*.

....

Instructions in accordance with the recommendations of Clause **24** of BS 5839-6: 2004 have been supplied to:*

Signed: ....   Date: ....

For and on behalf of: ....

* Where design, installation and commissioning are not all the responsibility of a single organization or person, the relevant words should be deleted. The signatory of the certificate should sign only as confirmation that the work for which they have been responsible complies with the relevant recommendations of BS 5839-6: 2004. A separate certificate(s) should then be issued for other work.

> *This certificate may be required by an authority responsible for enforcement of fire safety legislation, such as the building control authority or housing authority. The recipient of this certificate might rely on the certificate as evidence of compliance with legislation. Liability could arise on the part of any organization or person that issues a certificate without due care in ensuring its validity.*

Figure 7 Model certificate for Grades B, C, D, E and F systems

25. Testing, servicing and maintenance

In order to ensure that the system is maintained in a fully operational state and that any faults are detected within a reasonable period of their occurrence, it is necessary for the system to be tested by the occupants and, even in the case of simple systems comprising smoke alarms, given simple maintenance.

Since Grade A systems largely comply with the recommendations of BS 5839-1, these systems should be tested, serviced and maintained in accordance with the recommendations of that standard. This will necessitate weekly testing by the user and periodic servicing by a fire alarm maintenance contractor.

Part 1 recommends that the actual frequency of servicing should be based on a risk assessment, but that the periods between each service visit should not exceed six months. In practice, if a modern, fully monitored Grade A system is installed in a dwelling, six-monthly servicing is adequate. Accordingly, the slightly vague nature of the recommended frequency in Part 1 is made more specific in Part 6, which recommends six-monthly servicing for Grade A systems. For Grade A systems, a servicing certificate of the type recommended by Part 1 should be issued; this may be of value to an enforcing authority, such as in the case of an HMO.

The recommendations for servicing in Part 1 are quite detailed and include annual functional testing of all detectors; in practice, this constitutes the major element of work and it can be carried out as a full annual test of all detectors or, for example, testing of 50% of the detectors at the time of every six-monthly service visit.

In the case of all other systems described in the Code, it is recommended in clause 25 that the user carry out a weekly test by operating all alarm sounders. In the case of smoke alarms and heat alarms, this will involve a test operation of the sounder in each smoke and heat alarm; this may be accomplished by using the test button.

In the case of Grades B and C systems, the Code recommends that these should be serviced every six months in accordance with the supplier's instructions. The six-monthly servicing has a particular relevance in the case of Grade C systems that comprise integrated fire and intruder alarm systems, as normal practice in the intruder alarm industry is to service installations that have remote signalling every six months. The Code does not specifically recommend that, in Grades B and C systems, annual detector testing is carried out. It will be for the system supplier to determine the frequency of detector testing in these systems. However, the Code does recommend that, if undue deposits of dust or dirt are likely to accumulate before detectors are cleaned or charged at frequencies recommended by the supplier, more frequent cleaning or replacement should be carried out; this recommendation also applies to smoke alarms in Grades D, E and F systems.

With regard to smoke alarms, the Code recommends that these should be cleaned periodically in accordance with the manufacturer's instructions. Some manufacturers recommend the use of a vacuum cleaner for this purpose, but the Code is not specific and depends on the guidance of the manufacturer. As noted above, however, it is recommended that, if detectors are installed in a dusty or dirty environment, more frequent cleaning may be necessary.

Index of references to clauses of BS 5839-6

NOTES

NOTES

NOTES

NOTES